THE H.O.P.E. FORMULA
"The Ultimate Health Secret"

PERSONAL JOURNAL

By Brenda Watson, N.D.

This Journal Belongs To:

_____

THE H.O.P.E. FORMULA The Ultimate Health Secret

Renew Life Press

Copyright © 2006 by Brenda Watson

ISBN 0-9719309-6-1
UPC 6-31257-53458-3

For more information regarding this publication write to:
Renew Life Press and Information Services
2076 Sunnydale Blvd.
Clearwater, FL 33765
1-800-450-1784

Printed and assembled in the USA

THE H.O.P.E. FORMULA

High Fiber • Oils • Probiotics • Enzymes

TABLE OF CONTENTS

WELCOME BY BRENDA WATSON

I became aware after several years of lecturing across the country to thousands of people on the subject of digestive health, that a simple explanation of the digestive process was very much needed, in book form, along with pictures and charts, in order to make the subject real to people. The recognition of that need ultimately gave birth to The H.O.P.E. Formula: The Ultimate Health Secret, the book to which this journal serves as companion.

I created the H.O.P.E. Journal to help you monitor and optimize your intake of High Fiber, Omega-3 Oil, Probiotics and Enzymes. Following the H.O.P.E. formula means consuming adequate daily amounts of these important elements. While they are not as well known as vitamins and minerals, the H.O.P.E. elements are every bit as vital to your health and well-being. The H.O. P.E. formula provides essential nourishment to your body, helping you improve your digestion, which will have the net effect of preventing disease and assisting in the restoration of health. Following this formula can literally put HOPE back into your life, as it did for me.

During my own personal struggle to recover from chronic illness, I became aware of the vital role the digestive system plays in overall health. Changes in diet and lifestyle and the addition of appropriate nutritional supplements were key elements responsible for my recovery. Over the years, I've worked in and developed my own clinics that specialize in digestive health. I have watched many people regain their health and maintain it through the application of the same natural health principles I used to regain my own health. These principles are incorporated in the H.O.P.E. Formula.

Following a workable therapeutic program is only part of the solution. The other part is to understand the process and to integrate it into your life so that it becomes second nature to you, part of your daily routine. I developed this journal to provide you with your own personal record of daily fiber, essential oil, probiotic and enzyme intake over a 6-month period. By monitoring your day-to-day consumption of these vital food factors and correlating it with how you feel, you will be able to follow your progress on the road to wellness and see exactly what works best for you in terms of food choices, combinations and quantities.

It has been well demonstrated that the process of journaling has numerous benefits, including:

- Increased focus and motivation to stick with a program
- Enhanced goal achievement
- Better understanding of the task at hand

By making daily entries in this journal, you are essentially co-authoring this book with me by filling in the blanks and providing the relevant details as they pertain to YOU. Your recorded facts and observations will give new life and meaning to the information contained in The H.O.P.E. Formula: The Ultimate Health Secret. Your entries in this journal will personalize raw facts into dynamic, tried and true health principles that work for YOU.

As you progress in your journal entries, you will also be progressing in the creation of a healthier lifestyle. The food choice and supplement regimens that you'll be implementing as you apply the H.O.P.E. formula may be a bit new and overwhelming at first, but as you make these changes, you will find that they are actually quite simple. You will find that with the discipline of implementing these simple changes comes the thrill of achievement, the pride of accomplishment.

In no time, the H.O.P.E. formula will become an integral part of your daily routine, a healthy new habit. By the time you have completed this journal, you'll be on "auto-pilot," independently making healthy choices in terms of types and quantities of food supplements consumed daily to optimize your intake of fiber, oil, probiotics and enzymes. When you no longer need it, this journal will have fulfilled its purpose.

Brenda Watson

Brenda Watson, N.D.

How to use your H.O.P.E. Formula Journal

Description of Journal: The H.O.P.E. Formula Personal Journal is very easy to use. If you take a few moments to read the following tips, it will help you gain maximum benefits from this journal.

It is important to keep this journal with you at all times so you are able to accurately record your daily activities. In addition, by keeping this journal with you at all times you will be able to update the food listing in the back of the book with your daily food items.

Your H.O.P.E. Formula Personal Journal consists of three sections: Info and Guides, Personalized H.O.P.E. Formula, and H.O.P.E. Resources. The following paragraphs describe each page in detail.

1. Questionnaire: The questionnaire is comprised of four sections. Each sections deals with part of The H.O.P.E. Formula (fig. 1). For ease of use, we have arranged our questionnaire to ask questions about two key elements and then give you your score.

Scoring: Questions have two different types of scoring. The first type has multiple choices with a number in parenthesis (A). Once you have found your answer, place the corresponding number on the line (B). The second type of scoring is cumulative (C). You find how many of the answers apply to you and put in the number (D)

Once you have your score for each answer, you add them together to get a total. PLEASE NOTE: A LOWER SCORE IS BETTER. Using this total, refer to that section's scoring and find out where you place (E). Each section scoring is broken down into three categories: Ideal, Fair and Poor. Ideal means you are achieving the desired amount. "Fair" means you are achieving minimal amount, however, you need to get more. "Poor" means you are achieving below minimal amounts and need significant increases in this area.

(fig. 1)

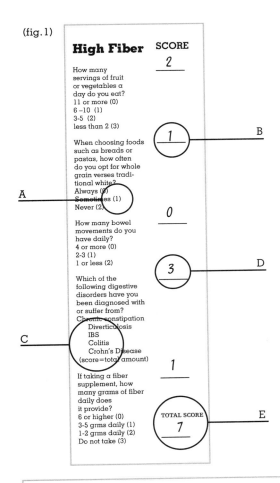

High Fiber   SCORE

2

How many
servings of fruit
or vegetables a
day do you eat?
11 or more (0)
6 –10 (1)
3-5 (2)
less than 2 (3)

1 — B

When choosing foods
such as breads or
pastas, how often
do you opt for whole
grain verses tradi-
tional white?
Always (0)
~~Sometimes~~ (1)
Never (2)

A —

0

How many bowel
movements do you
have daily?
4 or more (0)
2-3 (1)
1 or less (2)

3 — D

Which of the
following digestive
disorders have you
been diagnosed with
or suffer from?
Chronic constipation
Diverticulosis
IBS
Colitis
Crohn's Disease
(score=total amount)

C —

1

If taking a fiber
supplement, how
many grams of fiber
daily does
it provide?
6 or higher (0)
3-5 grms daily (1)
1-2 grms daily (2)
Do not take (3)

TOTAL SCORE — E
7

Questionnaire Scoring:

High Fiber

0-5 – If your score is from 0 to 5 you are in the "ideal" category. This means you are eating a diet high in fiber, have good bowel habits and/or may not suffer from digestive disorders. Keep up the good work!! A fiber supplement can still be helpful and add to the benefits you are receiving from your diet. We would suggest a supplement providing from 3 to 5 grams of fiber per serving, once or twice daily.

(fig. 2)

6-10 – If your score is from 6 to 10 you are in the "fair" category. This means although you try, you may not be getting the proper amount of fiber daily that you need for optimal health. Try to increase your fiber rich foods throughout the day. A fiber supplement can be of help in getting your daily needs. We would suggest a supplement providing from 3 to 5 grams per serving, at least twice daily, or a fiber rich bar that contains 14 grams of fiber, once daily.

11-15 – If your score is from 11 to 15 you are in the "poor" category. This means that your daily food choices do not contain needed fiber, or you may suffer from digestive disorders which may increase your daily need of fiber. Certainly try to increase your fiber rich foods everyday, using the guide in the back of this journal. We highly suggest a fiber supplement in the form of a fiber rich bar containing 14 grams of fiber, twice daily.

In the "Goal and Plan" section, use the information in the scoring area to help you develop a daily plan for each of the H.O.P.E. elements (fig 3).

Personalized Page

H   Goal: _To reach 35 or more grams of fiber daily._

    Plan: _Eat a high fiber breakfast each morning consisting of oatmeal, whole grain muffin or high fiber cereal. Eat a high fiber bar every day for a snack._

O   Goal: _To increase daily omega-3 intake to 2 or more grams._

    Plan: _Eat more wild salmon. Eat raw nuts for snacks. Take fish oil supplement daily._

P   Goal: _To get at least 6 billion cultures of good bacteria daily._

    Plan: _Eat plain yogurt every day as a snack. Take probiotic supplement daily._

E   Goal: _To reach 50% of diet as raw, enzyme rich foods._

    Plan: _Eat more raw foods with every meal. Eat salads for lunch. Take enzyme supplement with meals._

Notes:

(fig. 3)

2. Daily H.O.P.E. Records: This is by far, the most important and substantial section. Having this in mind, the guide for this section has been broken down into six sub sections. (fig 4)

A. The first section displays The H.O.P.E. Formula Daily Goal.

B. Section two allows you to fill in the date, the day in your program and the day of the week.

C. The third section allows you to track your H.O.P.E. consumption. There are three main meal sections (Breakfast, Lunch and Dinner) with each section having a snack area. For each meal, you are able to write in four rows and four columns tracking each part of the formula. To track your High Fiber or Oils, please fill in the appropriate quantity (in grams) for each item. Probiotics should be filled in with a value from 0-3 based on how that item is listed in the back of the journal. The last column is for Enzymes. In this column, place a check if the item contained Enzymes. If you have a snack before lunch, please fill in the "Snacks" area and use the tracking system described above. Once you have completed the Breakfast area, add up your totals. Use this process for Lunch and Dinner.

D. The Fourth section is for you to track your daily supplements. As you see, it is once again broken down into four rows and columns. This allows you to take a supplement for each part of the H.O.P.E. Formula.

E. In the fifth section, please add your meal column totals to your supplement totals and fill in the appropriate box. Please remember that Enzymes will have a check or no check for the day. In this section, you can also track how many 8 oz. glasses of water you have had.

F. The last section, Notes, allows you to add important information to remind you in the future.

H.O.P.E. Daily Goal - High Fiber : 35g. - Oils : 2g. - Probiotics : At least 6 Billion Cultures - Enzymes : with each Meal

Date: January 11	Day #: 2	Day of the week: Wednesday

FOOD	High Fiber	Omega-3 Oils	Probiotics	Enzymes
Breakfast amount				
1/2 cup steelcut oatmeal	9.0	0	0	
1/4 cup raisins	1.4	0.01	0	√
Snacks: 1/2 cup yogurt	0	0.06	3	√
Breakfast Totals:	10.4	0.07	3	√
Lunch amount				
2 cups romaine lettuce w/	9.0	0.11	0	√
1/2 med tomato	.75	0	0	√
1/2 cup chickpeas	6.25	0.03	0	
1/2 cup carrots	1.80	0	0	√
Snacks: 1/4 cup raw walnuts	1.5	2.27	0	√
Lunch Totals:	12.3	2.41	0	√
Dinner amount				
4 oz. broiled chicken	0	0.07	0	
1 cup spinach, cooked	4.3	0.15	0	
1 med sweet pot, cooked	3.8	0	0	
Snacks: 1 med apple	3.3	0.01	0	√
Dinner Totals:	11.4	0.23	0	√

Supplements

Description:	High Fiber	Oils	Probiotics	Enzymes
1 scoop fiber supp.	3.0			
1 fish oil supp.		1.0		
1 cap probiotic			12 bil	
3 caps enzyme				√

TODAY'S GRAND TOTALS

37.1 High Fiber	3+ Probiotics
3.71 Oils	√ Enzymes

8 oz. glasses of water consumed

X	X	X	X	X	X	X	X
☐	☐	☐	☐	☐	☐	☐	☐

Notes:

(fig 4)

3. H.O.P.E. Meals vs. Non H.O.P.E. Meals:

Use this page to see how you can have H.O.P.E. in each meal of your day. We have put meals into two columns for easy reference (Fig.5)

H.O.P.E. Meals vs. Non H.O.P.E. Meals

	H.O.P.E. meals	non-H.O.P.E. meals
Breakfast:	1/2 cup Steel Cut Oatmeal 1 cup mixed fruit 1 cup yogurt	Bacon and eggs White toast

(Fig.5)

4. How to Read a Food and Supplement Fact Panel:

This section explains what to look for in a food or supplement facts panel in relation to the H.O.P.E. Formula. To make this process easier we have highlighted key areas of the facts panel. This will help you to identify foods or supplements high in Fiber, Oils, Probiotics or Enzymes.

Nutrition Facts

Serving Size ½ cup (114g)
Servings Per Container 4

Amount Per Serving

Calories 90   Calories from Fat 30

	% Daily Value*
Total Fat 3g	**5%**
Saturated Fat 0g	**0%**
Cholesterol 0mg	**0%**
Sodium 300mg	**13%**
Total Carbohydrate 13g	**4%**
Dietary Fiber 3g	**12%**
Sugars 3g	
Protein 3g	

Vitamin A 80%	•	Vitamin C 60%
Calcium 4%	•	Iron 4%

(Fig. 6)

This is a sample of a nutritional facts panel from the US Food and Drug Administration (Fig. 6):

The Nutrition Labeling and Education Act of 1990 (NLEA) requires nutrition labeling for most foods (except meat and poultry). Highlighted here is the dietary fiber content of the represented food. When shopping for high H.O.P.E. foods, make sure to look at the Nutrition Facts Panel as it can offer valuable information. Not every food panel will show the omega-3, probiotic or enzyme content of foods. However, most panels will show the fiber content.

5. How to use the "Food List" section:

Favorite Food	Measure	Fiber	Omega-3 Oils	Probiotics	Enzymes
F & G		grams	grams	value 0-3	*
Figs, dried	2 figs	1.6	0	0	*

This section lists, alphabetically, some popular foods that are found in standard diets. Each item is identified with Fiber, Omega 3 Oil, Probiotic and Enzyme content (fig.7). Both Fiber and Omega 3 Oil content are given in grams. However, the probiotic content is given a value from 0-3 (as used in section 3 above) with 3 being the highest. This number identifies low to high probiotic content. The asterisk indicates that the food contains enzymes.

* All values are approximate according to the USDA National Nutrient Database unless otherwise noted.

(fig.7)

6. How to Graph your Progress section:

This section will allow you to track your daily progress visually. The left side of the graph is numbered from 1-4. This number represents how many parts of the formula (H.O.P.E.) that you achieved for that day. The bottom of the graph gives you a box to put in the date. Using the goals for each day and your daily grand totals, fill in the graph appropriately (fig. 8).

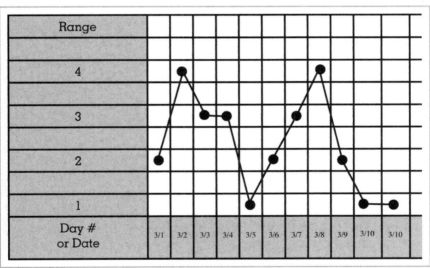

(fig.8)

PART II

PERSONALIZED H.O.P.E. FORMULA

H.O.P.E. QUESTIONNAIRE

High Fiber   SCORE

How many
servings of fruit
or vegetables a
day do you eat?
11 or more (0)
6 –10 (1)
3-5 (2)
less than 2 (3)

_____

When choosing foods
such as breads or
pastas, how often
do you opt for whole
grain verses tradi-
tional white?
Always (0)
Sometimes (1)
Never (2)

_____

How many bowel
movements do you
have daily?
4 or more (0)
2-3 (1)
1 or less (2)

_____

Which of the
following digestive
disorders have you
been diagnosed with
or suffer from?
Chronic constipation
    Diverticulosis
    IBS
    Colitis
    Crohn's Disease
(score=total amount)

_____

If taking a fiber
supplement, how
many grams of fiber
daily does
it provide?
6 or higher (0)
3-5 grms daily (1)
1-2 grms daily (2)
Do not take (3)

TOTAL SCORE

_____

Oils   SCORE

How many times
a week do you
eat fish?
3 or more (0)
1-2 (1)
None (2)

_____

What type of fish
do you normally
consume?
Salmon (0)
canned such as
sardines (1)
Mild white fish (2)

_____

Do you use raw oils
such as olive, flax or
borage daily?
Yes (0)
No (1)

_____

Which of
the following
cardiovascular
disorders have
you been diagnosed
with or suffer from?
Previous Heart Attack
Blocked Arteries
High Cholesterol
High Blood Pressure
(score=total amount)

_____

If taking an oil
supplement, how
many grams of oil
daily does it
provide?
5 or higher (0)
3-4 grms daily (1)
1-2 grms daily (2)
Do not take (3)

TOTAL SCORE

_____

Questionnaire Scoring:

High Fiber

0-5 – If your score is from 0 to 5 you are in the "ideal" category. This means you are eating a diet high in fiber, have good bowel habits and/or may not suffer from digestive disorders. Keep up the good work!! A fiber supplement can still be helpful and add to the benefits you are receiving from your diet. We would suggest a supplement providing from 3 to 5 grams of fiber per serving, once or twice daily.

6-10 – If your score is from 6 to 10 you are in the "fair" category. This means although you try, you may not be getting the proper amount of fiber daily that you need for optimal health. Try to increase your fiber rich foods throughout the day. A fiber supplement can be of help in getting your daily needs. We would suggest a supplement providing from 3 to 5 grams per serving, at least twice daily, or a fiber rich bar that contains 14 grams of fiber, once daily.

11-15 – If your score is from 11 to 15 you are in the "poor" category. This means that your daily food choices do not contain needed fiber, or you may suffer from digestive disorders which may increase your daily need of fiber. Certainly try to increase your fiber rich foods everyday, using the guide in the back of this journal. We highly suggest a fiber supplement in the form of a fiber rich bar containing 14 grams of fiber, twice daily.

Omega-3 Oils

0-4 – If your score is from 0 to 4 you are in the "ideal" category. This means your food choices reflect a high Omega-3 oil content and/or you may not suffer from digestive or cardiovascular disorders which can increase your need. Keep up the good work! An Omega-3 fatty acid supplement can still be helpful and add to the benefits you are receiving from your diet. We would suggest a concentrated fish oil supplement containing 300 EPA and 200 DHA per softgel; once daily.

5-8 – If your score is from 5 to 8 you are in the "fair" category. This means although you try, you may not be getting the proper amount of Omega-3 oil daily that you need for optimal health. Try to increase your Omega-3 foods, using the guide in the back of the journal. An Omega-3 oil supplement can be of help in getting your daily needs. We would suggest a concentrated fish oil supplement containing 300 EPA and 200 DHA per softgel, twice daily.

9-12 – If your score is from 9 to 12 you are in the "poor" category. This means your daily food choices do not contain the needed Omega-3 oils and/or you may suffer from cardiovascular or digestive disorders which can increase your daily need of Omega-3. Certainly, try to increase your Omega-3 rich foods everyday, using the guide in the back of this journal. We highly suggest an Omega-3 supplement. Try using a concentrated fish oil supplement containing 300 EPA and 200 DHA per softgel, three times daily.

Probiotics

SCORE

_____

How many foods daily do you eat containing natural friendly bacteria, such as yogurt, kefir or cultured vegetables?
4 or more (0)
1-3 (1)
None (2)

How many times a week do you eat sweets or high sugared foods?

_____

None (0)
1-2 times weekly (1)
3-4 times weekly (2)
More than 4
times weekly (3)

When was the last time you took antibiotics?

_____

More than 4 yrs ago (0)
within 1-3 yrs ago (1)
6 to 11 months (2)
currently taking (3)

Which of the following conditions do you experience frequently (more than once a year)?

_____

Sinus Infections
Respiratory Infections
Fungal/Yeast Infections
Digestive Disorder (e.g. diverticulosis, IBS, constipation)

If taking a probiotic (friendly bacteria) supplement, how many billions of cultures daily does it provide?

_____

More than 50 billion (0)
25-50 billion daily (1)
under 25 billion daily (2)
Do not take (3)

TOTAL SCORE

_____

Enzymes

SCORE

How often do you eat raw fruits or vegetables?

_____

Daily (0)
5-6 times weekly (1)
3-4 times weekly (2)
2 or less times weekly (3)

Which of the following conditions do you experience frequently (more than once a week)?

_____

Gas after eating
Bloating
Heartburn
Indigestion
Reflux

Do vegetables such as broccoli, cabbage, Brussels sprouts, or cauliflower give you digestive complaints?

_____

No (0)
Yes (1)

Do you often experience cramping and diarrhea after eating dairy products?

_____

No (0)
Yes (1)

Are you currently taking an enzyme supplement?

_____

Yes (0)
No (1)

TOTAL SCORE

_____

Questionnaire Scoring:

Probiotics

0-5 – If your score is from 0 to 5 you are in the "ideal" category. This means your food choices reflect a high amount of good bacteria and/or you may not suffer from conditions which can increase your need of probitotics. Keep up the good work! A probiotic supplement can still be helpful and add to the benefits you are receiving from your diet. We would suggest a probiotic supplement providing 6 billion cultures, once daily.

6 –10 – If your score is from 6 to 10 you are in the "fair" category. This means, although you try, you may not be getting the proper amount of probiotics daily that you need for optimal health. Try increasing foods naturally high in good bacteria like yogurt. We would suggest a probiotic supplement providing 6 billion cultures, twice daily.

11-15 – If your score is from 11 to 15 you are in the "poor" category. This means your daily food choices do not contain a high amount of the good bacteria and/or you may suffer from problems which can increase your need of probiotics. Increase your foods which naturally provide good bacteria, using the guide in the back of this journal. We highly suggest a probiotic supplement providing at least 6 billion cultures, three times daily. You may also benefit from a higher culture count probiotic, such as a 50 billion culture per capsule, once daily.

Omega-3 Oils

0-3 – If your score is from 0 to 3 you are in the "ideal" category. This means your food choices include lots of raw fruits and vegetables providing live enzymes daily, and/or you may not suffer from digestive complaints which can increase your need of enzymes. Keep up the good work! An enzyme supplement with meals can still be helpful and add to the benefits you are receiving from your diet. We would suggest one capsule of an enzyme supplement that includes protease, lipase and amylase with each meal.

4-7 – If your score is from 4 to 7 you are in the "fair" category. This means, although you try, you may not be getting enough enzyme rich foods in your diet and/or you may suffer from digestive complaints which can increase your need of enzymes. Try to include more raw fruits and/or vegetables with every meal. We would suggest one to two capsules of an enzyme supplement that includes protease, lipase and amylase with each meal. If you are having discomfort after eating dairy foods, we would suggest, in addition to the above, an enzyme with high amounts of lactase with dairy foods.

8-11 – If your score is from 8 to 11 you are in the "poor" category. This means your diet does not include many foods which contain live enzymes and/or you may suffer from several digestive complaints which can increase your need for enzymes. Using the guide in the back of the journal, increase your raw fruits and vegetables with every meal. We highly suggest two capsules of an enzyme supplement that includes protease, lipase and amylase with each meal. If you are having discomfort after eating dairy foods, we would suggest in addition to the above, an enzyme with high amounts of lactase with dairy foods.

Personalized Page

H   Goal: _____
_____
_____

Plan: _____
_____
_____

O   Goal: _____
_____
_____

Plan: _____
_____
_____

P   Goal: _____
_____
_____

Plan: _____
_____
_____

E   Goal: _____
_____
_____

Plan: _____
_____
_____

Notes: _____
_____
_____
_____

DAILY H.O.P.E. PROGRESS

H.O.P.E. Daily Goal - High Fiber : 35g. - Oils : 2g. - Probiotics : At least 6 Billion Cultures - Enzymes : with each Meal

Date:	Day #:		Day of the week:	

FOOD		High Fiber	Omega-3 Oils	Probiotics	Enzymes
Breakfast	amount				
Snacks:					
Breakfast Totals:					
Lunch	amount				
Snacks:					
Lunch Totals:					
Dinner	amount				
Snacks:					
Dinner Totals:					

Supplements

Description:	High Fiber	Oils	Probiotics	Enzymes

TODAY'S GRAND TOTALS

High Fiber	Probiotics
Oils	Enzymes

8 oz. glasses of water consumed

☐☐☐☐☐☐☐☐
☐☐☐☐☐☐☐☐

Notes:

Date:	Day #:	Day of the week:

FOOD		High Fiber	Omega-3 Oils	Probiotics	Enzymes

Breakfast — amount

Snacks:					
Breakfast Totals:					

Lunch — amount

Snacks:					
Lunch Totals:					

Dinner — amount

Snacks:					
Dinner Totals:					

Supplements

Description:	High Fiber	Oils	Probiotics	Enzymes

TODAY'S GRAND TOTALS

High Fiber	Probiotics
Oils	Enzymes

8 oz. glasses of water consumed

☐☐☐☐☐☐☐☐
☐☐☐☐☐☐☐☐

Notes:

H.O.P.E. Daily Goal - High Fiber : 35g. - Oils : 2g. - Probiotics : At least 6 Billion Cultures - Enzymes : with each Meal

| Date: | | Day #: | | | Day of the week: | | |

FOOD		High Fiber	Omega-3 Oils	Probiotics	Enzymes
Breakfast	amount				
Snacks:					
Breakfast Totals:					
Lunch	amount				
Snacks:					
Lunch Totals:					
Dinner	amount				
Snacks:					
Dinner Totals:					

Supplements

Description:	High Fiber	Oils	Probiotics	Enzymes

TODAY'S GRAND TOTALS

High Fiber	Probiotics
Oils	Enzymes

8 oz. glasses of water consumed
☐☐☐☐☐☐☐☐
☐☐☐☐☐☐☐☐

Notes:

H.O.P.E. Daily Goal - High Fiber : 35g. - Oils : 2g. - Probiotics : At least 6 Billion Cultures - Enzymes: with each Meal

Date:	Day #:	Day of the week:

FOOD		High Fiber	Omega-3 Oils	Probiotics	Enzymes
Breakfast	amount				
Snacks:					
Breakfast Totals:					
Lunch	amount				
Snacks:					
Lunch Totals:					
Dinner	amount				
Snacks:					
Dinner Totals:					

Supplements

Description:	High Fiber	Oils	Probiotics	Enzymes

TODAY'S GRAND TOTALS

High Fiber	Probiotics
Oils	Enzymes

8 oz. glasses of water consumed

☐☐☐☐☐☐☐
☐☐☐☐☐☐☐

Notes:

H.O.P.E. Daily Goal - High Fiber : 35g. - Oils : 2g. - Probiotics : At least 6 Billion Cultures - Enzymes : with each Meal

Date:	Day #:	Day of the week:

FOOD	High Fiber	Omega-3 Oils	Probiotics	Enzymes

Breakfast amount

Snacks:				
Breakfast Totals:				

Lunch amount

Snacks:				
Lunch Totals:				

Dinner amount

Snacks:				
Dinner Totals:				

Supplements

Description:	High Fiber	Oils	Probiotics	Enzymes

TODAY'S GRAND TOTALS

High Fiber	Probiotics
Oils	Enzymes

8 oz. glasses of water consumed
☐☐☐☐☐☐☐☐
☐☐☐☐☐☐☐☐

Notes:

H.O.P.E. Daily Goal - High Fiber : 35g. - Oils : 2g. - Probiotics : At least 6 Billion Cultures - Enzymes: with each Meal

Date:	Day #:	Day of the week:

FOOD	High Fiber	Omega-3 Oils	Probiotics	Enzymes
Breakfast amount				
Snacks:				
Breakfast Totals:				
Lunch amount				
Snacks:				
Lunch Totals:				
Dinner amount				
Snacks:				
Dinner Totals:				

Supplements

Description:	High Fiber	Oils	Probiotics	Enzymes

TODAY'S GRAND TOTALS

High Fiber	Probiotics

Oils	Enzymes

8 oz. glasses of water consumed

☐☐☐☐☐☐☐
☐☐☐☐☐☐☐

Notes:

H.O.P.E. Daily Goal - High Fiber : 35g. - Oils : 2g. - Probiotics : At least 6 Billion Cultures - Enzymes: with each Me

Date:	Day #:		Day of the week:	

FOOD		High Fiber	Omega-3 Oils	Probiotics	Enzymes
Breakfast	amount				
Snacks:					
Breakfast Totals:					
Lunch	amount				
Snacks:					
Lunch Totals:					
Dinner	amount				
Snacks:					
Dinner Totals:					

Supplements					
Description:		High Fiber	Oils	Probiotics	Enzymes

TODAY'S GRAND TOTALS

High Fiber	Probiotics
Oils	Enzymes

8 oz. glasses of water consumed

☐☐☐☐☐☐☐☐
☐☐☐☐☐☐☐☐

Notes:

H.O.P.E. Daily Goal - High Fiber : 35g. - Oils : 2g. - Probiotics : At least 6 Billion Cultures - Enzymes: with each Meal

Date:	Day #:		Day of the week:

FOOD	High Fiber	Omega-3 Oils	Probiotics	Enzymes
Breakfast amount				
Snacks:				
Breakfast Totals:				
Lunch amount				
Snacks:				
Lunch Totals:				
Dinner amount				
Snacks:				
Dinner Totals:				

Supplements					TODAY'S GRAND TOTALS
Description:	High Fiber	Oils	Probiotics	Enzymes	

TODAY'S GRAND TOTALS

High Fiber	Probiotics
Oils	Enzymes

8 oz. glasses of water consumed

☐☐☐☐☐☐☐☐
☐☐☐☐☐☐☐☐

Notes:

H.O.P.E. Daily Goal - High Fiber : 35g. - Oils : 2g. - Probiotics : At least 6 Billion Cultures - Enzymes: with each Meal

| Date: | Day #: | Day of the week: |

FOOD	High Fiber	Omega-3 Oils	Probiotics	Enzymes

Breakfast   amount

Snacks:				
Breakfast Totals:				

Lunch   amount

Snacks:				
Lunch Totals:				

Dinner   amount

Snacks:				
Dinner Totals:				

Supplements

Description:	High Fiber	Oils	Probiotics	Enzymes

TODAY'S GRAND TOTALS

High Fiber	Probiotics
Oils	Enzymes

8 oz. glasses of water consumed

☐ ☐ ☐ ☐ ☐ ☐ ☐ ☐
☐ ☐ ☐ ☐ ☐ ☐ ☐ ☐

Notes:

H.O.P.E. Daily Goal - High Fiber : 35g. - Oils : 2g. - Probiotics : At least 6 Billion Cultures - Enzymes : with each Meal

Date:	Day #:	Day of the week:

FOOD	High Fiber	Omega-3 Oils	Probiotics	Enzymes
Breakfast amount				
Snacks:				
Breakfast Totals:				
Lunch amount				
Snacks:				
Lunch Totals:				
Dinner amount				
Snacks:				
Dinner Totals:				

Supplements

Description:	High Fiber	Oils	Probiotics	Enzymes

TODAY'S GRAND TOTALS

High Fiber	Probiotics
Oils	Enzymes

8 oz. glasses of water consumed

☐☐☐☐☐☐☐☐
☐☐☐☐☐☐☐☐

Notes:

H.O.P.E. Daily Goal - High Fiber : 35g. - Oils : 2g. - Probiotics : At least 6 Billion Cultures - Enzymes: with each Meal

Date:		Day #:		Day of the week:	

FOOD		High Fiber	Omega-3 Oils	Probiotics	Enzymes
Breakfast	amount				
Snacks:					
Breakfast Totals:					
Lunch	amount				
Snacks:					
Lunch Totals:					
Dinner	amount				
Snacks:					
Dinner Totals:					

Supplements

Description:	High Fiber	Oils	Probiotics	Enzymes

TODAY'S GRAND TOTALS

High Fiber	Probiotics
Oils	Enzymes

8 oz. glasses of water consumed
☐☐☐☐☐☐☐
☐☐☐☐☐☐☐

Notes:

H.O.P.E. Daily Goal - High Fiber : 35g. - Oils : 2g. - Probiotics : At least 6 Billion Cultures - Enzymes: with each Meal

Date:	Day #:		Day of the week:

FOOD		High Fiber	Omega-3 Oils	Probiotics	Enzymes
Breakfast	amount				
Snacks:					
Breakfast Totals:					
Lunch	amount				
Snacks:					
Lunch Totals:					
Dinner	amount				
Snacks:					
Dinner Totals:					

Supplements					
Description:	High Fiber	Oils	Probiotics	Enzymes	

TODAY'S GRAND TOTALS

High Fiber	Probiotics
Oils	Enzymes

8 oz. glasses of water consumed

☐☐☐☐☐☐☐
☐☐☐☐☐☐☐

Notes:

Date:	Day #:	Day of the week:

FOOD		High Fiber	Omega-3 Oils	Probiotics	Enzymes

Breakfast — amount

Snacks:					
Breakfast Totals:					

Lunch — amount

Snacks:					
Lunch Totals:					

Dinner — amount

Snacks:					
Dinner Totals:					

Supplements

Description:	High Fiber	Oils	Probiotics	Enzymes

TODAY'S GRAND TOTALS

High Fiber	Probiotics
Oils	Enzymes

8 oz. glasses of water consumed

Notes:

H.O.P.E. Daily Goal - High Fiber : 35g. - Oils : 2g. - Probiotics : At least 6 Billion Cultures - Enzymes : with each Meal

Date:	Day #:	Day of the week:

FOOD	High Fiber	Omega-3 Oils	Probiotics	Enzymes

Breakfast — amount

Snacks:				
Breakfast Totals:				

Lunch — amount

Snacks:				
Lunch Totals:				

Dinner — amount

Snacks:				
Dinner Totals:				

Supplements

Description:	High Fiber	Oils	Probiotics	Enzymes

TODAY'S GRAND TOTALS

High Fiber	Probiotics
Oils	Enzymes

8 oz. glasses of water consumed

☐☐☐☐☐☐☐
☐☐☐☐☐☐☐

Notes:

H.O.P.E. Daily Goal - High Fiber : 35g. - Oils : 2g. - Probiotics : At least 6 Billion Cultures - Enzymes : with each Meal

Date:	Day #:	Day of the week:

FOOD		High Fiber	Omega-3 Oils	Probiotics	Enzymes
Breakfast	amount				
Snacks:					
Breakfast Totals:					
Lunch	amount				
Snacks:					
Lunch Totals:					
Dinner	amount				
Snacks:					
Dinner Totals:					

Supplements

Description:	High Fiber	Oils	Probiotics	Enzymes

TODAY'S GRAND TOTALS

High Fiber	Probiotics

Oils	Enzymes

8 oz. glasses of water consumed

☐☐☐☐☐☐☐☐
☐☐☐☐☐☐☐☐

Notes:

H.O.P.E. Daily Goal - High Fiber : 35g. - Oils : 2g. - Probiotics : At least 6 Billion Cultures - Enzymes : with each Meal

Date:	Day # :	Day of the week:

FOOD		High Fiber	Omega-3 Oils	Probiotics	Enzymes
Breakfast	amount				
Snacks:					
Breakfast Totals:					
Lunch	amount				
Snacks:					
Lunch Totals:					
Dinner	amount				
Snacks:					
Dinner Totals:					

Supplements

Description:	High Fiber	Oils	Probiotics	Enzymes

TODAY'S GRAND TOTALS

High Fiber	Probiotics
Oils	Enzymes

8 oz. glasses of water consumed

☐☐☐☐☐☐☐☐
☐☐☐☐☐☐☐☐

Notes:

H.O.P.E. Daily Goal - High Fiber : 35g. - Oils : 2g. - Probiotics : At least 6 Billion Cultures - Enzymes: with each Mec

Date:	Day #:		Day of the week:

FOOD	High Fiber	Omega-3 Oils	Probiotics	Enzymes

Breakfast amount

		High Fiber	Omega-3 Oils	Probiotics	Enzymes
Snacks:					
Breakfast Totals:					

Lunch amount

		High Fiber	Omega-3 Oils	Probiotics	Enzymes
Snacks:					
Lunch Totals:					

Dinner amount

		High Fiber	Omega-3 Oils	Probiotics	Enzymes
Snacks:					
Dinner Totals:					

Supplements

Description:	High Fiber	Oils	Probiotics	Enzymes

TODAY'S GRAND TOTALS

High Fiber	Probiotics
Oils	Enzymes

8 oz. glasses of water consumed

☐☐☐☐☐☐☐☐
☐☐☐☐☐☐☐☐

Notes:

H.O.P.E. Daily Goal - High Fiber : 35g. - Oils : 2g. - Probiotics : At least 6 Billion Cultures - Enzymes : with each Meal

Date:	Day #:		Day of the week:

FOOD		High Fiber	Omega-3 Oils	Probiotics	Enzymes
Breakfast	amount				
Snacks:					
Breakfast Totals:					
Lunch	amount				
Snacks:					
Lunch Totals:					
Dinner	amount				
Snacks:					
Dinner Totals:					

Supplements					
Description:	High Fiber	Oils	Probiotics	Enzymes

TODAY'S GRAND TOTALS

High Fiber	Probiotics
Oils	Enzymes

8 oz. glasses of water consumed

☐☐☐☐☐☐☐☐
☐☐☐☐☐☐☐☐

Notes:

H.O.P.E. Daily Goal - High Fiber : 35g. - Oils : 2g. - Probiotics : At least 6 Billion Cultures - Enzymes : with each Meal

Date:	Day #:	Day of the week:

FOOD	High Fiber	Omega-3 Oils	Probiotics	Enzymes

Breakfast amount

Snacks:				
Breakfast Totals:				

Lunch amount

Snacks:				
Lunch Totals:				

Dinner amount

Snacks:				
Dinner Totals:				

Supplements

Description:	High Fiber	Oils	Probiotics	Enzymes

TODAY'S GRAND TOTALS

High Fiber	Probiotics
Oils	Enzymes

8 oz. glasses of water consumed

☐☐☐☐☐☐☐☐
☐☐☐☐☐☐☐☐

Notes:

H.O.P.E. Daily Goal - High Fiber : 35g. - Oils : 2g. - Probiotics : At least 6 Billion Cultures - Enzymes: with each Meal

Date:	Day #:	Day of the week:

FOOD	High Fiber	Omega-3 Oils	Probiotics	Enzymes

Breakfast	amount				
Snacks:					
Breakfast Totals:					

Lunch	amount				
Snacks:					
Lunch Totals:					

Dinner	amount				
Snacks:					
Dinner Totals:					

Supplements

Description:	High Fiber	Oils	Probiotics	Enzymes

TODAY'S GRAND TOTALS

High Fiber	Probiotics
Oils	Enzymes

8 oz. glasses of water consumed

☐ ☐ ☐ ☐ ☐ ☐ ☐ ☐
☐ ☐ ☐ ☐ ☐ ☐ ☐ ☐

Notes:

H.O.P.E. Daily Goal - High Fiber : 35g. - Oils : 2g. - Probiotics : At least 6 Billion Cultures - Enzymes: with each Mea

Date:	Day #:	Day of the week:

FOOD		High Fiber	Omega-3 Oils	Probiotics	Enzymes
Breakfast	amount				
Snacks:					
Breakfast Totals:					
Lunch	amount				
Snacks:					
Lunch Totals:					
Dinner	amount				
Snacks:					
Dinner Totals:					

Supplements

Description:	High Fiber	Oils	Probiotics	Enzymes

TODAY'S GRAND TOTALS

High Fiber	Probiotics
Oils	Enzymes

8 oz. glasses of water consumed

☐☐☐☐☐☐☐
☐☐☐☐☐☐☐

Notes:

Date:	Day #:	Day of the week:

FOOD	High Fiber	Omega-3 Oils	Probiotics	Enzymes
Breakfast amount				
Snacks:				
Breakfast Totals:				
Lunch amount				
Snacks:				
Lunch Totals:				
Dinner amount				
Snacks:				
Dinner Totals:				

Supplements

Description:	High Fiber	Oils	Probiotics	Enzymes

TODAY'S GRAND TOTALS

High Fiber	Probiotics
Oils	Enzymes

8 oz. glasses of water consumed

☐ ☐ ☐ ☐ ☐ ☐ ☐ ☐
☐ ☐ ☐ ☐ ☐ ☐ ☐ ☐

Notes:

H.O.P.E. Daily Goal - High Fiber : 35g. - Oils : 2g. - Probiotics : At least 6 Billion Cultures - Enzymes: with each Med

| Date: | | Day #: | | Day of the week: | | |

FOOD		High Fiber	Omega-3 Oils	Probiotics	Enzymes
Breakfast	amount				
Snacks:					
Breakfast Totals:					
Lunch	amount				
Snacks:					
Lunch Totals:					
Dinner	amount				
Snacks:					
Dinner Totals:					

Supplements

Description:	High Fiber	Oils	Probiotics	Enzymes

TODAY'S GRAND TOTALS

High Fiber	Probiotics
Oils	Enzymes

8 oz. glasses of water consumed

☐☐☐☐☐☐☐
☐☐☐☐☐☐☐

Notes:

H.O.P.E. Daily Goal - High Fiber : 35g. - Oils : 2g. - Probiotics : At least 6 Billion Cultures - Enzymes: with each Meal

Date:	Day #:	Day of the week:

FOOD		High Fiber	Omega-3 Oils	Probiotics	Enzymes
Breakfast	amount				
Snacks:					
Breakfast Totals:					
Lunch	amount				
Snacks:					
Lunch Totals:					
Dinner	amount				
Snacks:					
Dinner Totals:					

Supplements					
Description:		High Fiber	Oils	Probiotics	Enzymes

TODAY'S GRAND TOTALS

High Fiber	Probiotics
Oils	Enzymes

8 oz. glasses of water consumed

☐☐☐☐☐☐☐☐
☐☐☐☐☐☐☐☐

Notes:

Date:	Day #:	Day of the week:

FOOD		High Fiber	Omega-3 Oils	Probiotics	Enzymes
Breakfast	amount				
Snacks:					
Breakfast Totals:					
Lunch	amount				
Snacks:					
Lunch Totals:					
Dinner	amount				
Snacks:					
Dinner Totals:					

Supplements

Description:	High Fiber	Oils	Probiotics	Enzymes

TODAY'S GRAND TOTALS

High Fiber	Probiotics
Oils	Enzymes

8 oz. glasses of water consumed

☐☐☐☐☐☐☐☐
☐☐☐☐☐☐☐☐

Notes:

H.O.P.E. Daily Goal - High Fiber : 35g. - Oils : 2g. - Probiotics : At least 6 Billion Cultures - Enzymes: with each Meal

Date:	Day #:	Day of the week:

FOOD		High Fiber	Omega-3 Oils	Probiotics	Enzymes

Breakfast
amount

Snacks:					
Breakfast Totals:					

Lunch
amount

Snacks:					
Lunch Totals:					

Dinner
amount

Snacks:					
Dinner Totals:					

Supplements

Description:	High Fiber	Oils	Probiotics	Enzymes

TODAY'S GRAND TOTALS

High Fiber	Probiotics
Oils	Enzymes

8 oz. glasses of water consumed

☐☐☐☐☐☐☐☐
☐☐☐☐☐☐☐☐

Notes:

H.O.P.E. Daily Goal - High Fiber : 35g. - Oils : 2g. - Probiotics : At least 6 Billion Cultures - Enzymes: with each Meal

Date:	Day #:	Day of the week:

FOOD		High Fiber	Omega-3 Oils	Probiotics	Enzymes
Breakfast	amount				
Snacks:					
Breakfast Totals:					
Lunch	amount				
Snacks:					
Lunch Totals:					
Dinner	amount				
Snacks:					
Dinner Totals:					

Supplements

Description:	High Fiber	Oils	Probiotics	Enzymes

TODAY'S GRAND TOTALS

High Fiber	Probiotics
Oils	Enzymes

8 oz. glasses of water consumed

☐☐☐☐☐☐☐
☐☐☐☐☐☐☐

Notes:

H.O.P.E. Daily Goal - High Fiber : 35g. - Oils : 2g. - Probiotics : At least 6 Billion Cultures - Enzymes: with each Meal

Date:	Day #:	Day of the week:

FOOD		High Fiber	Omega-3 Oils	Probiotics	Enzymes
Breakfast	amount				
Snacks:					
Breakfast Totals:					
Lunch	amount				
Snacks:					
Lunch Totals:					
Dinner	amount				
Snacks:					
Dinner Totals:					

Supplements				
Description:	High Fiber	Oils	Probiotics	Enzymes

TODAY'S GRAND TOTALS

High Fiber	Probiotics
Oils	Enzymes

8 oz. glasses of water consumed

☐☐☐☐☐☐☐☐
☐☐☐☐☐☐☐☐

Notes:

H.O.P.E. Daily Goal - High Fiber : 35g. - Oils : 2g. - Probiotics : At least 6 Billion Cultures - Enzymes: with each Meal

Date: _____ Day #: _____ Day of the week: _____

FOOD	High Fiber	Omega-3 Oils	Probiotics	Enzymes
Breakfast amount				
Snacks:				
Breakfast Totals:				
Lunch amount				
Snacks:				
Lunch Totals:				
Dinner amount				
Snacks:				
Dinner Totals:				

Supplements

Description:	High Fiber	Oils	Probiotics	Enzymes

TODAY'S GRAND TOTALS

High Fiber	Probiotics
Oils	Enzymes

8 oz. glasses of water consumed
☐☐☐☐☐☐☐☐
☐☐☐☐☐☐☐☐

Notes:

H.O.P.E. Daily Goal - High Fiber : 35g. - Oils : 2g. - Probiotics : At least 6 Billion Cultures - Enzymes: with each Meal

Date:	Day #:		Day of the week:

FOOD		High Fiber	Omega-3 Oils	Probiotics	Enzymes
Breakfast	amount				
Snacks:					
Breakfast Totals:					
Lunch	amount				
Snacks:					
Lunch Totals:					
Dinner	amount				
Snacks:					
Dinner Totals:					

Supplements					
Description:	High Fiber	Oils	Probiotics	Enzymes	

TODAY'S GRAND TOTALS

High Fiber	Probiotics
Oils	Enzymes

8 oz. glasses of water consumed

☐ ☐ ☐ ☐ ☐ ☐ ☐
☐ ☐ ☐ ☐ ☐ ☐ ☐

Notes:

H.O.P.E. Daily Goal - High Fiber : 35g. - Oils : 2g. - Probiotics : At least 6 Billion Cultures - Enzymes : with each Meal

Date:	Day #:		Day of the week:	

FOOD		High Fiber	Omega-3 Oils	Probiotics	Enzymes
Breakfast	amount				
Snacks:					
Breakfast Totals:					
Lunch	amount				
Snacks:					
Lunch Totals:					
Dinner	amount				
Snacks:					
Dinner Totals:					

Supplements

Description:	High Fiber	Oils	Probiotics	Enzymes

TODAY'S GRAND TOTALS

High Fiber	Probiotics
Oils	Enzymes

8 oz. glasses of water consumed

☐ ☐ ☐ ☐ ☐ ☐ ☐
☐ ☐ ☐ ☐ ☐ ☐ ☐

Notes:

H.O.P.E. Daily Goal - High Fiber : 35g. - Oils : 2g. - Probiotics : At least 6 Billion Cultures - Enzymes: with each Meal

Date:	Day #:	Day of the week:

FOOD		High Fiber	Omega-3 Oils	Probiotics	Enzymes
Breakfast	amount				
Snacks:					
Breakfast Totals:					
Lunch	amount				
Snacks:					
Lunch Totals:					
Dinner	amount				
Snacks:					
Dinner Totals:					

Supplements					
Description:	High Fiber	Oils	Probiotics	Enzymes	

TODAY'S GRAND TOTALS

High Fiber	Probiotics
Oils	Enzymes

8 oz. glasses of water consumed

☐☐☐☐☐☐☐☐
☐☐☐☐☐☐☐☐

Notes:

H.O.P.E. Daily Goal - High Fiber : 35g. - Oils : 2g. - Probiotics : At least 6 Billion Cultures - Enzymes: with each Meal

Date:	Day #:		Day of the week:			

FOOD		High Fiber	Omega-3 Oils	Probiotics	Enzymes
Breakfast	amount				
Snacks:					
Breakfast Totals:					
Lunch	amount				
Snacks:					
Lunch Totals:					
Dinner	amount				
Snacks:					
Dinner Totals:					

Supplements

Description:	High Fiber	Oils	Probiotics	Enzymes

TODAY'S GRAND TOTALS

High Fiber	Probiotics
Oils	Enzymes

8 oz. glasses of water consumed

☐☐☐☐☐☐☐☐
☐☐☐☐☐☐☐☐

Notes:

H.O.P.E. Daily Goal - High Fiber : 35g. - Oils : 2g. - Probiotics : At least 6 Billion Cultures - Enzymes: with each Meal

Date:	Day #:	Day of the week:

FOOD		High Fiber	Omega-3 Oils	Probiotics	Enzymes
Breakfast	amount				
Snacks:					
Breakfast Totals:					
Lunch	amount				
Snacks:					
Lunch Totals:					
Dinner	amount				
Snacks:					
Dinner Totals:					

Supplements

Description:	High Fiber	Oils	Probiotics	Enzymes

TODAY'S GRAND TOTALS

High Fiber	Probiotics
Oils	Enzymes

8 oz. glasses of water consumed

☐☐☐☐☐☐☐
☐☐☐☐☐☐☐

Notes:

H.O.P.E. Daily Goal - High Fiber : 35g. - Oils : 2g. - Probiotics : At least 6 Billion Cultures - Enzymes: with each Med

Date:	Day #:	Day of the week:

FOOD		High Fiber	Omega-3 Oils	Probiotics	Enzymes
Breakfast	amount				
Snacks:					
Breakfast Totals:					
Lunch	amount				
Snacks:					
Lunch Totals:					
Dinner	amount				
Snacks:					
Dinner Totals:					

Supplements

Description:	High Fiber	Oils	Probiotics	Enzymes

TODAY'S GRAND TOTALS

High Fiber	Probiotics
Oils	Enzymes

8 oz. glasses of water consumed

☐☐☐☐☐☐☐☐
☐☐☐☐☐☐☐☐

Notes:

H.O.P.E. Daily Goal - High Fiber : 35g. - Oils : 2g. - Probiotics : At least 6 Billion Cultures - Enzymes: with each Meal

Date:	Day #:	Day of the week:

FOOD		High Fiber	Omega-3 Oils	Probiotics	Enzymes
Breakfast	amount				
Snacks:					
Breakfast Totals:					
Lunch	amount				
Snacks:					
Lunch Totals:					
Dinner	amount				
Snacks:					
Dinner Totals:					

Supplements

Description:	High Fiber	Oils	Probiotics	Enzymes

TODAY'S GRAND TOTALS

High Fiber	Probiotics
Oils	Enzymes

8 oz. glasses of water consumed

☐☐☐☐☐☐☐☐
☐☐☐☐☐☐☐☐

Notes:

H.O.P.E. Daily Goal - High Fiber : 35g. - Oils : 2g. - Probiotics : At least 6 Billion Cultures - Enzymes: with each Meal

Date:	Day #:	Day of the week:

FOOD		High Fiber	Omega-3 Oils	Probiotics	Enzymes

Breakfast — amount

Snacks:					
Breakfast Totals:					

Lunch — amount

Snacks:					
Lunch Totals:					

Dinner — amount

Snacks:					
Dinner Totals:					

Supplements

Description:	High Fiber	Oils	Probiotics	Enzymes

TODAY'S GRAND TOTALS

High Fiber	Probiotics
Oils	Enzymes

8 oz. glasses of water consumed

☐☐☐☐☐☐☐☐
☐☐☐☐☐☐☐☐

Notes:

H.O.P.E. Daily Goal - High Fiber : 35g. - Oils : 2g. - Probiotics : At least 6 Billion Cultures - Enzymes: with each Meal

Date:	Day #:	Day of the week:

FOOD		High Fiber	Omega-3 Oils	Probiotics	Enzymes
Breakfast	amount				
Snacks:					
Breakfast Totals:					
Lunch	amount				
Snacks:					
Lunch Totals:					
Dinner	amount				
Snacks:					
Dinner Totals:					

Supplements

Description:	High Fiber	Oils	Probiotics	Enzymes

TODAY'S GRAND TOTALS

High Fiber	Probiotics

Oils	Enzymes

8 oz. glasses of water consumed

☐☐☐☐☐☐☐☐
☐☐☐☐☐☐☐☐

Notes:

H.O.P.E. Daily Goal - High Fiber : 35g. - Oils : 2g. - Probiotics : At least 6 Billion Cultures - Enzymes: with each Meal

Date:	Day #:	Day of the week:

FOOD	High Fiber	Omega-3 Oils	Probiotics	Enzymes
Breakfast amount				
Snacks:				
Breakfast Totals:				
Lunch amount				
Snacks:				
Lunch Totals:				
Dinner amount				
Snacks:				
Dinner Totals:				

Supplements

Description:	High Fiber	Oils	Probiotics	Enzymes

TODAY'S GRAND TOTALS

High Fiber   Probiotics

Oils   Enzymes

8 oz. glasses of water consumed

☐☐☐☐☐☐☐
☐☐☐☐☐☐☐

Notes:

H.O.P.E. Daily Goal - High Fiber : 35g. - Oils : 2g. - Probiotics : At least 6 Billion Cultures - Enzymes: with each Meal

Date:	Day #:	Day of the week:

FOOD		High Fiber	Omega-3 Oils	Probiotics	Enzymes
Breakfast	amount				
Snacks:					
Breakfast Totals:					
Lunch	amount				
Snacks:					
Lunch Totals:					
Dinner	amount				
Snacks:					
Dinner Totals:					

Supplements				
Description:	High Fiber	Oils	Probiotics	Enzymes

TODAY'S GRAND TOTALS

High Fiber	Probiotics

Oils	Enzymes

8 oz. glasses of water consumed

☐☐☐☐☐☐☐☐
☐☐☐☐☐☐☐☐

Notes:

H.O.P.E. Daily Goal - High Fiber : 35g. - Oils : 2g. - Probiotics : At least 6 Billion Cultures - Enzymes: with each Mea

Date:	Day #:		Day of the week:		

FOOD		High Fiber	Omega-3 Oils	Probiotics	Enzymes
Breakfast	amount				
Snacks:					
Breakfast Totals:					
Lunch	amount				
Snacks:					
Lunch Totals:					
Dinner	amount				
Snacks:					
Dinner Totals:					

Supplements

Description:	High Fiber	Oils	Probiotics	Enzymes

TODAY'S GRAND TOTALS

High Fiber	Probiotics
Oils	Enzymes

8 oz. glasses of water consumed

☐ ☐ ☐ ☐ ☐ ☐ ☐
☐ ☐ ☐ ☐ ☐ ☐ ☐

Notes:

H.O.P.E. Daily Goal - High Fiber : 35g. - Oils : 2g. - Probiotics : At least 6 Billion Cultures - Enzymes: with each Meal

Date:	Day #:		Day of the week:		

FOOD	High Fiber	Omega-3 Oils	Probiotics	Enzymes

Breakfast
amount

Snacks:				
Breakfast Totals:				

Lunch
amount

Snacks:				
Lunch Totals:				

Dinner
amount

Snacks:				
Dinner Totals:				

Supplements

Description:	High Fiber	Oils	Probiotics	Enzymes

TODAY'S GRAND TOTALS

High Fiber	Probiotics
Oils	Enzymes

8 oz. glasses of water consumed
☐ ☐ ☐ ☐ ☐ ☐ ☐
☐ ☐ ☐ ☐ ☐ ☐ ☐

Notes:

Date:	Day #:		Day of the week:	

FOOD		High Fiber	Omega-3 Oils	Probiotics	Enzymes
Breakfast	amount				
Snacks:					
Breakfast Totals:					
Lunch	amount				
Snacks:					
Lunch Totals:					
Dinner	amount				
Snacks:					
Dinner Totals:					

Supplements

Description:	High Fiber	Oils	Probiotics	Enzymes

TODAY'S GRAND TOTALS

High Fiber	Probiotics
Oils	Enzymes

8 oz. glasses of water consumed

☐☐☐☐☐☐☐☐
☐☐☐☐☐☐☐☐

Notes:

H.O.P.E. Daily Goal - High Fiber : 35g. - Oils : 2g. - Probiotics : At least 6 Billion Cultures - Enzymes: with each Meal

Date:	Day #:	Day of the week:

FOOD	High Fiber	Omega-3 Oils	Probiotics	Enzymes
Breakfast amount				
Snacks:				
Breakfast Totals:				
Lunch amount				
Snacks:				
Lunch Totals:				
Dinner amount				
Snacks:				
Dinner Totals:				

Supplements

Description:	High Fiber	Oils	Probiotics	Enzymes

TODAY'S GRAND TOTALS

High Fiber	Probiotics
Oils	Enzymes

8 oz. glasses of water consumed

☐ ☐ ☐ ☐ ☐ ☐ ☐ ☐
☐ ☐ ☐ ☐ ☐ ☐ ☐ ☐

Notes:

H.O.P.E. Daily Goal - High Fiber : 35g. - Oils : 2g. - Probiotics : At least 6 Billion Cultures - Enzymes: with each Mea

Date: Day #:   Day of the week:

FOOD	High Fiber	Omega-3 Oils	Probiotics	Enzymes
Breakfast amount				
Snacks:				
Breakfast Totals:				
Lunch amount				
Snacks:				
Lunch Totals:				
Dinner amount				
Snacks:				
Dinner Totals:				

Supplements

Description:	High Fiber	Oils	Probiotics	Enzymes

TODAY'S GRAND TOTALS

High Fiber	Probiotics

Oils	Enzymes

8 oz. glasses of water consumed

☐☐☐☐☐☐☐☐
☐☐☐☐☐☐☐☐

Notes:

H.O.P.E. Daily Goal - High Fiber : 35g. - Oils : 2g. - Probiotics : At least 6 Billion Cultures - Enzymes : with each Meal

Date:	Day #:	Day of the week:

FOOD		High Fiber	Omega-3 Oils	Probiotics	Enzymes
Breakfast	amount				
Snacks:					
Breakfast Totals:					
Lunch	amount				
Snacks:					
Lunch Totals:					
Dinner	amount				
Snacks:					
Dinner Totals:					

Supplements				
Description:	High Fiber	Oils	Probiotics	Enzymes

TODAY'S GRAND TOTALS

High Fiber	Probiotics

Oils	Enzymes

8 oz. glasses of water consumed

☐☐☐☐☐☐☐
☐☐☐☐☐☐☐

Notes:

H.O.P.E. Daily Goal - High Fiber : 35g. - Oils : 2g. - Probiotics : At least 6 Billion Cultures - Enzymes: with each Meal

Date:	Day #:	Day of the week:

FOOD	High Fiber	Omega-3 Oils	Probiotics	Enzymes
Breakfast amount				
Snacks:				
Breakfast Totals:				
Lunch amount				
Snacks:				
Lunch Totals:				
Dinner amount				
Snacks:				
Dinner Totals:				

Supplements

Description:	High Fiber	Oils	Probiotics	Enzymes

TODAY'S GRAND TOTALS

High Fiber	Probiotics
Oils	Enzymes

8 oz. glasses of water consumed

☐☐☐☐☐☐☐
☐☐☐☐☐☐☐

Notes:

Date:	Day #:		Day of the week:	

FOOD		High Fiber	Omega-3 Oils	Probiotics	Enzymes

Breakfast   amount

Snacks:					
Breakfast Totals:					

Lunch   amount

Snacks:					
Lunch Totals:					

Dinner   amount

Snacks:					
Dinner Totals:					

Supplements

Description:	High Fiber	Oils	Probiotics	Enzymes

TODAY'S GRAND TOTALS

High Fiber	Probiotics
Oils	Enzymes

8 oz. glasses of water consumed

☐☐☐☐☐☐☐
☐☐☐☐☐☐☐

Notes:

Date: Day #:   Day of the week:

FOOD		High Fiber	Omega-3 Oils	Probiotics	Enzymes
Breakfast	amount				
Snacks:					
Breakfast Totals:					
Lunch	amount				
Snacks:					
Lunch Totals:					
Dinner	amount				
Snacks:					
Dinner Totals:					

Supplements

Description:	High Fiber	Oils	Probiotics	Enzymes

TODAY'S GRAND TOTALS

High Fiber	Probiotics
Oils	Enzymes

8 oz. glasses of water consumed

☐☐☐☐☐☐☐
☐☐☐☐☐☐☐

Notes:

H.O.P.E. Daily Goal - High Fiber : 35g. - Oils : 2g. - Probiotics : At least 6 Billion Cultures - Enzymes: with each Meal

Date:	Day #:		Day of the week:

FOOD			High Fiber	Omega-3 Oils	Probiotics	Enzymes
Breakfast	amount					
Snacks:						
Breakfast Totals:						
Lunch	amount					
Snacks:						
Lunch Totals:						
Dinner	amount					
Snacks:						
Dinner Totals:						

Supplements

Description:	High Fiber	Oils	Probiotics	Enzymes

TODAY'S GRAND TOTALS

High Fiber	Probiotics
Oils	Enzymes

8 oz. glasses of water consumed

☐ ☐ ☐ ☐ ☐ ☐ ☐
☐ ☐ ☐ ☐ ☐ ☐ ☐

Notes:

Date:	Day #:		Day of the week:

FOOD		High Fiber	Omega-3 Oils	Probiotics	Enzymes
Breakfast	amount				
Snacks:					
Breakfast Totals:					
Lunch	amount				
Snacks:					
Lunch Totals:					
Dinner	amount				
Snacks:					
Dinner Totals:					

Supplements

Description:	High Fiber	Oils	Probiotics	Enzymes

TODAY'S GRAND TOTALS

High Fiber	Probiotics
Oils	Enzymes

8 oz. glasses of water consumed

☐☐☐☐☐☐☐
☐☐☐☐☐☐☐

Notes:

H.O.P.E. Daily Goal - High Fiber : 35g. - Oils : 2g. - Probiotics : At least 6 Billion Cultures - Enzymes: with each Meal

Date:	Day #:	Day of the week:

FOOD	High Fiber	Omega-3 Oils	Probiotics	Enzymes
Breakfast amount				
Snacks:				
Breakfast Totals:				
Lunch amount				
Snacks:				
Lunch Totals:				
Dinner amount				
Snacks:				
Dinner Totals:				

Supplements				
Description:	High Fiber	Oils	Probiotics	Enzymes

TODAY'S GRAND TOTALS

High Fiber	Probiotics
Oils	Enzymes

8 oz. glasses of water consumed

☐☐☐☐☐☐☐☐
☐☐☐☐☐☐☐☐

Notes:

H.O.P.E. Daily Goal - High Fiber : 35g. - Oils : 2g. - Probiotics : At least 6 Billion Cultures - Enzymes: with each Meal

Date:	Day #:	Day of the week:

FOOD		High Fiber	Omega-3 Oils	Probiotics	Enzymes
Breakfast	amount				
Snacks:					
Breakfast Totals:					
Lunch	amount				
Snacks:					
Lunch Totals:					
Dinner	amount				
Snacks:					
Dinner Totals:					

Supplements

Description:	High Fiber	Oils	Probiotics	Enzymes

TODAY'S GRAND TOTALS

High Fiber	Probiotics
Oils	Enzymes

8 oz. glasses of water consumed

☐☐☐☐☐☐☐☐
☐☐☐☐☐☐☐☐

Notes:

H.O.P.E. Daily Goal - High Fiber : 35g. - Oils : 2g. - Probiotics : At least 6 Billion Cultures - Enzymes: with each Meal

Date:	Day #:	Day of the week:

FOOD		High Fiber	Omega-3 Oils	Probiotics	Enzymes
Breakfast	amount				
Snacks:					
Breakfast Totals:					
Lunch	amount				
Snacks:					
Lunch Totals:					
Dinner	amount				
Snacks:					
Dinner Totals:					

Supplements

Description:	High Fiber	Oils	Probiotics	Enzymes

TODAY'S GRAND TOTALS

High Fiber	Probiotics

Oils	Enzymes

8 oz. glasses of water consumed

☐☐☐☐☐☐☐☐
☐☐☐☐☐☐☐☐

Notes:

H.O.P.E. Daily Goal - High Fiber : 35g. - Oils : 2g. - Probiotics : At least 6 Billion Cultures - Enzymes: with each Mea

Date:	Day #:	Day of the week:

FOOD	High Fiber	Omega-3 Oils	Probiotics	Enzymes

Breakfast — amount

Snacks:				
Breakfast Totals:				

Lunch — amount

Snacks:				
Lunch Totals:				

Dinner — amount

Snacks:				
Dinner Totals:				

Supplements

Description:	High Fiber	Oils	Probiotics	Enzymes

TODAY'S GRAND TOTALS

High Fiber	Probiotics
Oils	Enzymes

8 oz. glasses of water consumed

☐ ☐ ☐ ☐ ☐ ☐ ☐ ☐
☐ ☐ ☐ ☐ ☐ ☐ ☐ ☐

Notes:

H.O.P.E. Daily Goal - High Fiber : 35g. - Oils : 2g. - Probiotics : At least 6 Billion Cultures - Enzymes: with each Meal

Date: Day #:   Day of the week:

FOOD		High Fiber	Omega-3 Oils	Probiotics	Enzymes
Breakfast	amount				
Snacks:					
Breakfast Totals:					
Lunch	amount				
Snacks:					
Lunch Totals:					
Dinner	amount				
Snacks:					
Dinner Totals:					

Supplements					
Description:	High Fiber	Oils	Probiotics	Enzymes	

TODAY'S GRAND TOTALS

High Fiber	Probiotics
Oils	Enzymes

8 oz. glasses of water consumed

☐ ☐ ☐ ☐ ☐ ☐ ☐ ☐
☐ ☐ ☐ ☐ ☐ ☐ ☐ ☐

Notes:

H.O.P.E. Daily Goal - High Fiber : 35g. - Oils : 2g. - Probiotics : At least 6 Billion Cultures - Enzymes: with each Meal

Date:	Day #:	Day of the week:

FOOD		High Fiber	Omega-3 Oils	Probiotics	Enzymes
Breakfast	amount				
Snacks:					
Breakfast Totals:					
Lunch	amount				
Snacks:					
Lunch Totals:					
Dinner	amount				
Snacks:					
Dinner Totals:					

Supplements

Description:	High Fiber	Oils	Probiotics	Enzymes

TODAY'S GRAND TOTALS

High Fiber	Probiotics
Oils	Enzymes

8 oz. glasses of water consumed
☐☐☐☐☐☐☐☐
☐☐☐☐☐☐☐☐

Notes:

H.O.P.E. Daily Goal - High Fiber : 35g. - Oils : 2g. - Probiotics : At least 6 Billion Cultures - Enzymes: with each Meal

Date: **Day #:**   **Day of the week:**

FOOD		High Fiber	Omega-3 Oils	Probiotics	Enzymes
Breakfast	amount				
Snacks:					
Breakfast Totals:					
Lunch	amount				
Snacks:					
Lunch Totals:					
Dinner	amount				
Snacks:					
Dinner Totals:					

Supplements

Description:	High Fiber	Oils	Probiotics	Enzymes

TODAY'S GRAND TOTALS

High Fiber	Probiotics
Oils	Enzymes

8 oz. glasses of water consumed

☐ ☐ ☐ ☐ ☐ ☐ ☐
☐ ☐ ☐ ☐ ☐ ☐ ☐

Notes:

H.O.P.E. Daily Goal - High Fiber : 35g. - Oils : 2g. - Probiotics : At least 6 Billion Cultures - Enzymes: with each Mea

Date:	Day #:	Day of the week:

FOOD		High Fiber	Omega-3 Oils	Probiotics	Enzymes
Breakfast	amount				
Snacks:					
Breakfast Totals:					
Lunch	amount				
Snacks:					
Lunch Totals:					
Dinner	amount				
Snacks:					
Dinner Totals:					

Supplements

Description:	High Fiber	Oils	Probiotics	Enzymes

TODAY'S GRAND TOTALS

High Fiber	Probiotics
Oils	Enzymes

8 oz. glasses of water consumed

☐ ☐ ☐ ☐ ☐ ☐ ☐
☐ ☐ ☐ ☐ ☐ ☐ ☐

Notes:

H.O.P.E. Daily Goal - High Fiber : 35g. - Oils : 2g. - Probiotics : At least 6 Billion Cultures - Enzymes: with each Meal

Date:	Day #:	Day of the week:

FOOD		High Fiber	Omega-3 Oils	Probiotics	Enzymes
Breakfast	amount				
Snacks:					
Breakfast Totals:					
Lunch	amount				
Snacks:					
Lunch Totals:					
Dinner	amount				
Snacks:					
Dinner Totals:					

Supplements					
Description:		High Fiber	Oils	Probiotics	Enzymes

TODAY'S GRAND TOTALS

High Fiber	Probiotics
Oils	Enzymes

8 oz. glasses of water consumed

☐☐☐☐☐☐☐
☐☐☐☐☐☐☐

Notes:

H.O.P.E. Daily Goal - High Fiber : 35g. - Oils : 2g. - Probiotics : At least 6 Billion Cultures - Enzymes: with each Meal

Date:	Day #:		Day of the week:

FOOD		High Fiber	Omega-3 Oils	Probiotics	Enzymes
Breakfast	amount				
Snacks:					
Breakfast Totals:					
Lunch	amount				
Snacks:					
Lunch Totals:					
Dinner	amount				
Snacks:					
Dinner Totals:					

Supplements

Description:	High Fiber	Oils	Probiotics	Enzymes

TODAY'S GRAND TOTALS

High Fiber	Probiotics
Oils	Enzymes

8 oz. glasses of water consumed

☐☐☐☐☐☐☐☐
☐☐☐☐☐☐☐☐

Notes:

H.O.P.E. Daily Goal - High Fiber : 35g. - Oils : 2g. - Probiotics : At least 6 Billion Cultures - Enzymes: with each Meal

Date:	Day #:		Day of the week:

FOOD	High Fiber	Omega-3 Oils	Probiotics	Enzymes

Breakfast — amount

		High Fiber	Omega-3 Oils	Probiotics	Enzymes
Snacks:					
Breakfast Totals:					

Lunch — amount

		High Fiber	Omega-3 Oils	Probiotics	Enzymes
Snacks:					
Lunch Totals:					

Dinner — amount

		High Fiber	Omega-3 Oils	Probiotics	Enzymes
Snacks:					
Dinner Totals:					

Supplements

Description:	High Fiber	Oils	Probiotics	Enzymes

TODAY'S GRAND TOTALS

High Fiber	Probiotics
Oils	Enzymes

8 oz. glasses of water consumed

☐ ☐ ☐ ☐ ☐ ☐ ☐
☐ ☐ ☐ ☐ ☐ ☐ ☐

Notes:

Date: **Day #:**   **Day of the week:**

FOOD	High Fiber	Omega-3 Oils	Probiotics	Enzymes
Breakfast *amount*				
Snacks:				
Breakfast Totals:				
Lunch *amount*				
Snacks:				
Lunch Totals:				
Dinner *amount*				
Snacks:				
Dinner Totals:				

Supplements

Description:	High Fiber	Oils	Probiotics	Enzymes

TODAY'S GRAND TOTALS

High Fiber	Probiotics
Oils	Enzymes

8 oz. glasses of water consumed

☐☐☐☐☐☐☐☐
☐☐☐☐☐☐☐☐

Notes:

H.O.P.E. Daily Goal - High Fiber : 35g. - Oils : 2g. - Probiotics : At least 6 Billion Cultures - Enzymes: with each Meal

Date:	Day #:	Day of the week:

FOOD	High Fiber	Omega-3 Oils	Probiotics	Enzymes
Breakfast amount				
Snacks:				
Breakfast Totals:				
Lunch amount				
Snacks:				
Lunch Totals:				
Dinner amount				
Snacks:				
Dinner Totals:				

Supplements

Description:	High Fiber	Oils	Probiotics	Enzymes

TODAY'S GRAND TOTALS

High Fiber	Probiotics
Oils	Enzymes

8 oz. glasses of water consumed

☐☐☐☐☐☐☐☐
☐☐☐☐☐☐☐☐

Notes:

Date:	Day #:		Day of the week:

FOOD		High Fiber	Omega-3 Oils	Probiotics	Enzymes

Breakfast	amount				
Snacks:					
Breakfast Totals:					

Lunch	amount				
Snacks:					
Lunch Totals:					

Dinner	amount				
Snacks:					
Dinner Totals:					

Supplements

Description:	High Fiber	Oils	Probiotics	Enzymes

TODAY'S GRAND TOTALS

High Fiber	Probiotics

Oils	Enzymes

8 oz. glasses of water consumed

☐☐☐☐☐☐☐
☐☐☐☐☐☐☐

Notes:

H.O.P.E. Daily Goal - High Fiber : 35g. - Oils : 2g. - Probiotics : At least 6 Billion Cultures - Enzymes: with each Meal

Date:	Day #:	Day of the week:

FOOD

		High Fiber	Omega-3 Oils	Probiotics	Enzymes

Breakfast   amount

Snacks:					
Breakfast Totals:					

Lunch   amount

Snacks:					
Lunch Totals:					

Dinner   amount

Snacks:					
Dinner Totals:					

Supplements

Description:	High Fiber	Oils	Probiotics	Enzymes

TODAY'S GRAND TOTALS

High Fiber	Probiotics
Oils	Enzymes

8 oz. glasses of water consumed

☐ ☐ ☐ ☐ ☐ ☐ ☐ ☐
☐ ☐ ☐ ☐ ☐ ☐ ☐ ☐

Notes:

H.O.P.E. Daily Goal - High Fiber : 35g. - Oils : 2g. - Probiotics : At least 6 Billion Cultures - Enzymes : with each Me

Date:	Day #:		Day of the week:		

FOOD	High Fiber	Omega-3 Oils	Probiotics	Enzymes
Breakfast amount				
Snacks:				
Breakfast Totals:				
Lunch amount				
Snacks:				
Lunch Totals:				
Dinner amount				
Snacks:				
Dinner Totals:				

Supplements				
Description:	High Fiber	Oils	Probiotics	Enzymes

TODAY'S GRAND TOTALS

High Fiber	Probiotics
Oils	Enzymes

8 oz. glasses of water consumed

☐☐☐☐☐☐☐☐
☐☐☐☐☐☐☐☐

Notes:

Date:	Day #:	Day of the week:

FOOD	High Fiber	Omega-3 Oils	Probiotics	Enzymes

Breakfast   amount

Snacks:				
Breakfast Totals:				

Lunch   amount

Snacks:				
Lunch Totals:				

Dinner   amount

Snacks:				
Dinner Totals:				

Supplements

Description:	High Fiber	Oils	Probiotics	Enzymes

TODAY'S GRAND TOTALS

High Fiber	Probiotics

Oils	Enzymes

8 oz. glasses of water consumed

☐ ☐ ☐ ☐ ☐ ☐ ☐
☐ ☐ ☐ ☐ ☐ ☐ ☐

Notes:

H.O.P.E. Daily Goal - High Fiber : 35g. - Oils : 2g. - Probiotics : At least 6 Billion Cultures - Enzymes : with each Me

Date:	Day #:	Day of the week:

FOOD		High Fiber	Omega-3 Oils	Probiotics	Enzymes
Breakfast	amount				
Snacks:					
Breakfast Totals:					
Lunch	amount				
Snacks:					
Lunch Totals:					
Dinner	amount				
Snacks:					
Dinner Totals:					

Supplements

Description:	High Fiber	Oils	Probiotics	Enzymes

TODAY'S GRAND TOTALS

High Fiber	Probiotics

Oils	Enzymes

8 oz. glasses of water consumed

☐☐☐☐☐☐☐☐
☐☐☐☐☐☐☐☐

Notes:

H.O.P.E. Daily Goal - High Fiber : 35g. - Oils : 2g. - Probiotics : At least 6 Billion Cultures - Enzymes : with each Meal

Date:	Day #:	Day of the week:

FOOD	High Fiber	Omega-3 Oils	Probiotics	Enzymes

Breakfast — amount

Snacks:				
Breakfast Totals:				

Lunch — amount

Snacks:				
Lunch Totals:				

Dinner — amount

Snacks:				
Dinner Totals:				

Supplements

Description:	High Fiber	Oils	Probiotics	Enzymes

TODAY'S GRAND TOTALS

High Fiber	Probiotics
Oils	Enzymes

8 oz. glasses of water consumed

☐☐☐☐☐☐☐☐
☐☐☐☐☐☐☐☐

Notes:

Date:	Day #:		Day of the week:		

FOOD		High Fiber	Omega-3 Oils	Probiotics	Enzymes
Breakfast	amount				
Snacks:					
Breakfast Totals:					
Lunch	amount				
Snacks:					
Lunch Totals:					
Dinner	amount				
Snacks:					
Dinner Totals:					

Supplements

Description:	High Fiber	Oils	Probiotics	Enzymes

TODAY'S GRAND TOTALS

High Fiber	Probiotics
Oils	Enzymes

8 oz. glasses of water consumed

☐☐☐☐☐☐☐☐
☐☐☐☐☐☐☐☐

Notes:

Date:	Day #:	Day of the week:

FOOD		High Fiber	Omega-3 Oils	Probiotics	Enzymes

Breakfast — amount

Snacks:					
Breakfast Totals:					

Lunch — amount

Snacks:					
Lunch Totals:					

Dinner — amount

Snacks:					
Dinner Totals:					

Supplements

Description:	High Fiber	Oils	Probiotics	Enzymes

TODAY'S GRAND TOTALS

High Fiber	Probiotics
Oils	Enzymes

8 oz. glasses of water consumed

☐☐☐☐☐☐☐☐
☐☐☐☐☐☐☐☐

Notes:

Date:	Day #:	Day of the week:

FOOD		High Fiber	Omega-3 Oils	Probiotics	Enzymes
Breakfast	amount				
Snacks:					
Breakfast Totals:					
Lunch	amount				
Snacks:					
Lunch Totals:					
Dinner	amount				
Snacks:					
Dinner Totals:					

Supplements

TODAY'S GRAND TOTALS

Description:	High Fiber	Oils	Probiotics	Enzymes

High Fiber	Probiotics
Oils	Enzymes

8 oz. glasses of water consumed

☐ ☐ ☐ ☐ ☐ ☐ ☐
☐ ☐ ☐ ☐ ☐ ☐ ☐

Notes:

H.O.P.E. Daily Goal - High Fiber : 35g. - Oils : 2g. - Probiotics : At least 6 Billion Cultures - Enzymes: with each Meal

Date:	Day #:	Day of the week:

FOOD		High Fiber	Omega-3 Oils	Probiotics	Enzymes

Breakfast amount

Snacks:					
Breakfast Totals:					

Lunch amount

Snacks:					
Lunch Totals:					

Dinner amount

Snacks:					
Dinner Totals:					

Supplements

Description:	High Fiber	Oils	Probiotics	Enzymes

TODAY'S GRAND TOTALS

High Fiber	Probiotics
Oils	Enzymes

8 oz. glasses of water consumed

☐☐☐☐☐☐☐
☐☐☐☐☐☐☐

Notes:

Date:	Day #:	Day of the week:

FOOD		High Fiber	Omega-3 Oils	Probiotics	Enzymes

Breakfast — amount

Snacks:				
Breakfast Totals:				

Lunch — amount

Snacks:				
Lunch Totals:				

Dinner — amount

Snacks:				
Dinner Totals:				

Supplements

Description:	High Fiber	Oils	Probiotics	Enzymes

TODAY'S GRAND TOTALS

High Fiber	Probiotics
Oils	Enzymes

8 oz. glasses of water consumed

☐☐☐☐☐☐☐☐
☐☐☐☐☐☐☐☐

Notes:

H.O.P.E. Daily Goal - High Fiber : 35g. - Oils : 2g. - Probiotics : At least 6 Billion Cultures - Enzymes: with each Meal

Date:	Day #:	Day of the week:

FOOD		High Fiber	Omega-3 Oils	Probiotics	Enzymes
Breakfast	amount				
Snacks:					
Breakfast Totals:					
Lunch	amount				
Snacks:					
Lunch Totals:					
Dinner	amount				
Snacks:					
Dinner Totals:					

Supplements					
Description:	High Fiber	Oils	Probiotics	Enzymes	

TODAY'S GRAND TOTALS

High Fiber	Probiotics

Oils	Enzymes

8 oz. glasses of water consumed

☐ ☐ ☐ ☐ ☐ ☐ ☐ ☐
☐ ☐ ☐ ☐ ☐ ☐ ☐ ☐

Notes:

H.O.P.E. Daily Goal - High Fiber : 35g. - Oils : 2g. - Probiotics : At least 6 Billion Cultures - Enzymes: with each Meal

Date:	Day #:		Day of the week:

FOOD		High Fiber	Omega-3 Oils	Probiotics	Enzymes
Breakfast	amount				
Snacks:					
Breakfast Totals:					
Lunch	amount				
Snacks:					
Lunch Totals:					
Dinner	amount				
Snacks:					
Dinner Totals:					

Supplements

Description:	High Fiber	Oils	Probiotics	Enzymes

TODAY'S GRAND TOTALS

High Fiber	Probiotics
Oils	Enzymes

8 oz. glasses of water consumed

☐ ☐ ☐ ☐ ☐ ☐ ☐
☐ ☐ ☐ ☐ ☐ ☐ ☐

Notes:

H.O.P.E. Daily Goal - High Fiber : 35g. - Oils : 2g. - Probiotics : At least 6 Billion Cultures - Enzymes: with each Meal

Date:	Day #:	Day of the week:

FOOD		High Fiber	Omega-3 Oils	Probiotics	Enzymes
Breakfast	amount				
Snacks:					
Breakfast Totals:					
Lunch	amount				
Snacks:					
Lunch Totals:					
Dinner	amount				
Snacks:					
Dinner Totals:					

Supplements

Description:	High Fiber	Oils	Probiotics	Enzymes

TODAY'S GRAND TOTALS

High Fiber	Probiotics
Oils	Enzymes

8 oz. glasses of water consumed

☐☐☐☐☐☐☐☐
☐☐☐☐☐☐☐☐

Notes:

H.O.P.E. Daily Goal - High Fiber : 35g. - Oils : 2g. - Probiotics : At least 6 Billion Cultures - Enzymes: with each Meal

Date:	Day #:	Day of the week:

FOOD		High Fiber	Omega-3 Oils	Probiotics	Enzymes
Breakfast	amount				
Snacks:					
Breakfast Totals:					
Lunch	amount				
Snacks:					
Lunch Totals:					
Dinner	amount				
Snacks:					
Dinner Totals:					

Supplements

Description:	High Fiber	Oils	Probiotics	Enzymes

TODAY'S GRAND TOTALS

High Fiber	Probiotics
Oils	Enzymes

8 oz. glasses of water consumed

☐☐☐☐☐☐☐☐
☐☐☐☐☐☐☐☐

Notes:

H.O.P.E. Daily Goal - High Fiber : 35g. - Oils : 2g. - Probiotics : At least 6 Billion Cultures - Enzymes: with each Meal

Date:	Day #:	Day of the week:

FOOD		High Fiber	Omega-3 Oils	Probiotics	Enzymes
Breakfast	amount				
Snacks:					
Breakfast Totals:					
Lunch	amount				
Snacks:					
Lunch Totals:					
Dinner	amount				
Snacks:					
Dinner Totals:					

Supplements

Description:	High Fiber	Oils	Probiotics	Enzymes

TODAY'S GRAND TOTALS

High Fiber	Probiotics
Oils	Enzymes

8 oz. glasses of water consumed

☐ ☐ ☐ ☐ ☐ ☐ ☐
☐ ☐ ☐ ☐ ☐ ☐ ☐

Notes:

Date:	Day #:		Day of the week:		

FOOD		High Fiber	Omega-3 Oils	Probiotics	Enzymes
Breakfast	amount				
Snacks:					
Breakfast Totals:					
Lunch	amount				
Snacks:					
Lunch Totals:					
Dinner	amount				
Snacks:					
Dinner Totals:					

Supplements

Description:	High Fiber	Oils	Probiotics	Enzymes

TODAY'S GRAND TOTALS

High Fiber	Probiotics
Oils	Enzymes

8 oz. glasses of water consumed

☐☐☐☐☐☐☐☐
☐☐☐☐☐☐☐☐

Notes:

H.O.P.E. Daily Goal - High Fiber : 35g. - Oils : 2g. - Probiotics : At least 6 Billion Cultures - Enzymes: with each Meal

Date:	Day #:		Day of the week:

FOOD		High Fiber	Omega-3 Oils	Probiotics	Enzymes
Breakfast	amount				
Snacks:					
Breakfast Totals:					
Lunch	amount				
Snacks:					
Lunch Totals:					
Dinner	amount				
Snacks:					
Dinner Totals:					

Supplements

Description:	High Fiber	Oils	Probiotics	Enzymes

TODAY'S GRAND TOTALS

High Fiber	Probiotics
Oils	Enzymes

8 oz. glasses of water consumed

☐ ☐ ☐ ☐ ☐ ☐ ☐
☐ ☐ ☐ ☐ ☐ ☐ ☐

Notes:

H.O.P.E. Daily Goal - High Fiber : 35g. - Oils : 2g. - Probiotics : At least 6 Billion Cultures - Enzymes: with each Meal

Date:		Day #:		Day of the week:		

FOOD		High Fiber	Omega-3 Oils	Probiotics	Enzymes

Breakfast — amount

Snacks:					
Breakfast Totals:					

Lunch — amount

Snacks:					
Lunch Totals:					

Dinner — amount

Snacks:					
Dinner Totals:					

Supplements

Description:	High Fiber	Oils	Probiotics	Enzymes

TODAY'S GRAND TOTALS

High Fiber	Probiotics
Oils	Enzymes

8 oz. glasses of water consumed

☐☐☐☐☐☐☐☐
☐☐☐☐☐☐☐☐

Notes:

H.O.P.E. Daily Goal - High Fiber : 35g. - Oils : 2g. - Probiotics : At least 6 Billion Cultures - Enzymes: with each Meal

Date:	Day #:	Day of the week:

FOOD		High Fiber	Omega-3 Oils	Probiotics	Enzymes
Breakfast	amount				
Snacks:					
Breakfast Totals:					
Lunch	amount				
Snacks:					
Lunch Totals:					
Dinner	amount				
Snacks:					
Dinner Totals:					

Supplements

Description:	High Fiber	Oils	Probiotics	Enzymes

TODAY'S GRAND TOTALS

High Fiber	Probiotics
Oils	Enzymes

8 oz. glasses of water consumed

☐☐☐☐☐☐☐☐
☐☐☐☐☐☐☐☐

Notes:

Date:	Day #:	Day of the week:

FOOD		High Fiber	Omega-3 Oils	Probiotics	Enzymes

Breakfast   amount

Snacks:					
Breakfast Totals:					

Lunch   amount

Snacks:					
Lunch Totals:					

Dinner   amount

Snacks:					
Dinner Totals:					

Supplements

Description:	High Fiber	Oils	Probiotics	Enzymes

TODAY'S GRAND TOTALS

High Fiber	Probiotics
Oils	Enzymes

8 oz. glasses of water consumed

☐☐☐☐☐☐☐
☐☐☐☐☐☐☐

Notes:

H.O.P.E. Daily Goal - High Fiber : 35g. - Oils : 2g. - Probiotics : At least 6 Billion Cultures - Enzymes: with each Meal

Date:	Day #:	Day of the week:

FOOD

	amount	High Fiber	Omega-3 Oils	Probiotics	Enzymes
Breakfast					
Snacks:					
Breakfast Totals:					
Lunch					
Snacks:					
Lunch Totals:					
Dinner					
Snacks:					
Dinner Totals:					

Supplements

Description:	High Fiber	Oils	Probiotics	Enzymes

TODAY'S GRAND TOTALS

High Fiber	Probiotics
Oils	Enzymes

8 oz. glasses of water consumed

☐ ☐ ☐ ☐ ☐ ☐ ☐ ☐
☐ ☐ ☐ ☐ ☐ ☐ ☐ ☐

Notes:

H.O.P.E. Daily Goal - High Fiber : 35g. - Oils : 2g. - Probiotics : At least 6 Billion Cultures - Enzymes: with each Med

Date:	Day #:	Day of the week:

FOOD	High Fiber	Omega-3 Oils	Probiotics	Enzymes

Breakfast	amount				
Snacks:					
Breakfast Totals:					

Lunch	amount				
Snacks:					
Lunch Totals:					

Dinner	amount				
Snacks:					
Dinner Totals:					

Supplements

Description:	High Fiber	Oils	Probiotics	Enzymes

TODAY'S GRAND TOTALS

High Fiber	Probiotics
Oils	Enzymes

8 oz. glasses of water consumed

☐☐☐☐☐☐☐
☐☐☐☐☐☐☐☐

Notes:

H.O.P.E. Daily Goal - High Fiber : 35g. - Oils : 2g. - Probiotics : At least 6 Billion Cultures - Enzymes : with each Meal

Date:	Day #:	Day of the week:

FOOD		High Fiber	Omega-3 Oils	Probiotics	Enzymes
Breakfast	amount				
Snacks:					
Breakfast Totals:					
Lunch	amount				
Snacks:					
Lunch Totals:					
Dinner	amount				
Snacks:					
Dinner Totals:					

Supplements						TODAY'S GRAND TOTALS
Description:	High Fiber	Oils	Probiotics	Enzymes		

TODAY'S GRAND TOTALS

High Fiber	Probiotics
Oils	Enzymes

8 oz. glasses of water consumed

Notes:

H.O.P.E. Daily Goal - High Fiber : 35g. - Oils : 2g. - Probiotics : At least 6 Billion Cultures - Enzymes: with each Mea

Date:	Day #:	Day of the week:			

FOOD	High Fiber	Omega-3 Oils	Probiotics	Enzymes
Breakfast amount				
Snacks:				
Breakfast Totals:				
Lunch amount				
Snacks:				
Lunch Totals:				
Dinner amount				
Snacks:				
Dinner Totals:				

Supplements				
Description:	High Fiber	Oils	Probiotics	Enzymes

TODAY'S GRAND TOTALS

High Fiber	Probiotics
Oils	Enzymes

8 oz. glasses of water consumed

☐ ☐ ☐ ☐ ☐ ☐ ☐ ☐
☐ ☐ ☐ ☐ ☐ ☐ ☐ ☐

Notes:

H.O.P.E. Daily Goal - High Fiber : 35g. - Oils : 2g. - Probiotics : At least 6 Billion Cultures - Enzymes : with each Meal

Date:	Day #:	Day of the week:

FOOD		High Fiber	Omega-3 Oils	Probiotics	Enzymes
Breakfast	amount				
Snacks:					
Breakfast Totals:					
Lunch	amount				
Snacks:					
Lunch Totals:					
Dinner	amount				
Snacks:					
Dinner Totals:					

Supplements

Description:	High Fiber	Oils	Probiotics	Enzymes

TODAY'S GRAND TOTALS

High Fiber	Probiotics
Oils	Enzymes

8 oz. glasses of water consumed

☐ ☐ ☐ ☐ ☐ ☐ ☐ ☐
☐ ☐ ☐ ☐ ☐ ☐ ☐ ☐

Notes:

H.O.P.E. Daily Goal - High Fiber : 35g. - Oils : 2g. - Probiotics : At least 6 Billion Cultures - Enzymes: with each Meal

Date:	Day #:	Day of the week:

FOOD	High Fiber	Omega-3 Oils	Probiotics	Enzymes

Breakfast — amount

	High Fiber	Omega-3 Oils	Probiotics	Enzymes
Snacks:				
Breakfast Totals:				

Lunch — amount

	High Fiber	Omega-3 Oils	Probiotics	Enzymes
Snacks:				
Lunch Totals:				

Dinner — amount

	High Fiber	Omega-3 Oils	Probiotics	Enzymes
Snacks:				
Dinner Totals:				

Supplements

Description:	High Fiber	Oils	Probiotics	Enzymes

TODAY'S GRAND TOTALS

High Fiber	Probiotics
Oils	Enzymes

8 oz. glasses of water consumed
☐☐☐☐☐☐☐☐
☐☐☐☐☐☐☐☐

Notes:

H.O.P.E. Daily Goal - High Fiber : 35g. - Oils : 2g. - Probiotics : At least 6 Billion Cultures - Enzymes: with each Meal

Date:	Day #:	Day of the week:

FOOD		High Fiber	Omega-3 Oils	Probiotics	Enzymes
Breakfast	amount				
Snacks:					
Breakfast Totals:					
Lunch	amount				
Snacks:					
Lunch Totals:					
Dinner	amount				
Snacks:					
Dinner Totals:					

Supplements					
Description:	High Fiber	Oils	Probiotics	Enzymes	

TODAY'S GRAND TOTALS

High Fiber	Probiotics
Oils	Enzymes

8 oz. glasses of water consumed

☐☐☐☐☐☐☐☐
☐☐☐☐☐☐☐☐

Notes:

Date:	Day #:	Day of the week:		

FOOD		High Fiber	Omega-3 Oils	Probiotics	Enzymes

Breakfast amount

Snacks:				
Breakfast Totals:				

Lunch amount

Snacks:				
Lunch Totals:				

Dinner amount

Snacks:				
Dinner Totals:				

Supplements

Description:	High Fiber	Oils	Probiotics	Enzymes

TODAY'S GRAND TOTALS

High Fiber	Probiotics
Oils	Enzymes

8 oz. glasses of water consumed

☐ ☐ ☐ ☐ ☐ ☐ ☐ ☐
☐ ☐ ☐ ☐ ☐ ☐ ☐ ☐

Notes:

H.O.P.E. Daily Goal - High Fiber : 35g. - Oils : 2g. - Probiotics : At least 6 Billion Cultures - Enzymes: with each Meal

Date:	Day #:	Day of the week:

FOOD	High Fiber	Omega-3 Oils	Probiotics	Enzymes

Breakfast   amount

	High Fiber	Oils	Probiotics	Enzymes
Snacks:				
Breakfast Totals:				

Lunch   amount

	High Fiber	Oils	Probiotics	Enzymes
Snacks:				
Lunch Totals:				

Dinner   amount

	High Fiber	Oils	Probiotics	Enzymes
Snacks:				
Dinner Totals:				

Supplements

Description:	High Fiber	Oils	Probiotics	Enzymes

TODAY'S GRAND TOTALS

High Fiber	Probiotics
Oils	Enzymes

8 oz. glasses of water consumed

☐☐☐☐☐☐☐
☐☐☐☐☐☐☐

Notes:

Date:	Day #:		Day of the week:

FOOD	High Fiber	Omega-3 Oils	Probiotics	Enzymes

Breakfast — amount

	High Fiber	Omega-3 Oils	Probiotics	Enzymes
Snacks:				
Breakfast Totals:				

Lunch — amount

	High Fiber	Omega-3 Oils	Probiotics	Enzymes
Snacks:				
Lunch Totals:				

Dinner — amount

	High Fiber	Omega-3 Oils	Probiotics	Enzymes
Snacks:				
Dinner Totals:				

Supplements

Description:	High Fiber	Oils	Probiotics	Enzymes

TODAY'S GRAND TOTALS

High Fiber	Probiotics
Oils	Enzymes

8 oz. glasses of water consumed

☐☐☐☐☐☐☐
☐☐☐☐☐☐☐

Notes:

H.O.P.E. Daily Goal - High Fiber : 35g. - Oils : 2g. - Probiotics : At least 6 Billion Cultures - Enzymes: with each Meal

Date:	Day #:	Day of the week:

FOOD		High Fiber	Omega-3 Oils	Probiotics	Enzymes
Breakfast	amount				
Snacks:					
Breakfast Totals:					
Lunch	amount				
Snacks:					
Lunch Totals:					
Dinner	amount				
Snacks:					
Dinner Totals:					

Supplements					
Description:	High Fiber	Oils	Probiotics	Enzymes

TODAY'S GRAND TOTALS

High Fiber	Probiotics
Oils	Enzymes

8 oz. glasses of water consumed

☐☐☐☐☐☐☐☐
☐☐☐☐☐☐☐☐

Notes:

H.O.P.E. Daily Goal - High Fiber : 35g. - Oils : 2g. - Probiotics : At least 6 Billion Cultures - Enzymes: with each Mea

| Date: | Day #: | | Day of the week: |

FOOD		High Fiber	Omega-3 Oils	Probiotics	Enzymes
Breakfast	amount				
Snacks:					
Breakfast Totals:					
Lunch	amount				
Snacks:					
Lunch Totals:					
Dinner	amount				
Snacks:					
Dinner Totals:					

Supplements

Description:	High Fiber	Oils	Probiotics	Enzymes

TODAY'S GRAND TOTALS

High Fiber	Probiotics
Oils	Enzymes

8 oz. glasses of water consumed

☐☐☐☐☐☐☐☐
☐☐☐☐☐☐☐☐

Notes:

Date:	Day #:		Day of the week:

FOOD		High Fiber	Omega-3 Oils	Probiotics	Enzymes
Breakfast	amount				
Snacks:					
Breakfast Totals:					
Lunch	amount				
Snacks:					
Lunch Totals:					
Dinner	amount				
Snacks:					
Dinner Totals:					

Supplements					
Description:	High Fiber	Oils	Probiotics	Enzymes	

TODAY'S GRAND TOTALS

High Fiber	Probiotics
Oils	Enzymes

8 oz. glasses of water consumed

☐ ☐ ☐ ☐ ☐ ☐ ☐
☐ ☐ ☐ ☐ ☐ ☐ ☐

Notes:

Date:		Day #:		Day of the week:	

FOOD		High Fiber	Omega-3 Oils	Probiotics	Enzymes

Breakfast	amount				
Snacks:					
Breakfast Totals:					

Lunch	amount				
Snacks:					
Lunch Totals:					

Dinner	amount				
Snacks:					
Dinner Totals:					

Supplements

Description:	High Fiber	Oils	Probiotics	Enzymes

TODAY'S GRAND TOTALS

High Fiber	Probiotics
Oils	Enzymes

8 oz. glasses of water consumed

☐☐☐☐☐☐☐
☐☐☐☐☐☐☐

Notes:

H.O.P.E. Daily Goal - High Fiber : 35g. - Oils : 2g. - Probiotics : At least 6 Billion Cultures - Enzymes: with each Meal

Date:	Day #:	Day of the week:

FOOD		High Fiber	Omega-3 Oils	Probiotics	Enzymes
Breakfast	amount				
Snacks:					
Breakfast Totals:					
Lunch	amount				
Snacks:					
Lunch Totals:					
Dinner	amount				
Snacks:					
Dinner Totals:					

Supplements

Description:	High Fiber	Oils	Probiotics	Enzymes

TODAY'S GRAND TOTALS

High Fiber	Probiotics
Oils	Enzymes

8 oz. glasses of water consumed

☐☐☐☐☐☐☐☐
☐☐☐☐☐☐☐☐

Notes:

H.O.P.E. Daily Goal - High Fiber : 35g. - Oils : 2g. - Probiotics : At least 6 Billion Cultures - Enzymes : with each Mea

Date:	Day #:	Day of the week:

FOOD		High Fiber	Omega-3 Oils	Probiotics	Enzymes

Breakfast — amount

Snacks:					
Breakfast Totals:					

Lunch — amount

Snacks:					
Lunch Totals:					

Dinner — amount

Snacks:					
Dinner Totals:					

Supplements

Description:	High Fiber	Oils	Probiotics	Enzymes

TODAY'S GRAND TOTALS

High Fiber	Probiotics

Oils	Enzymes

8 oz. glasses of water consumed

☐ ☐ ☐ ☐ ☐ ☐ ☐
☐ ☐ ☐ ☐ ☐ ☐ ☐

Notes:

H.O.P.E. Daily Goal - High Fiber : 35g. - Oils : 2g. - Probiotics : At least 6 Billion Cultures - Enzymes: with each Meal

Date:	Day #:	Day of the week:

FOOD		High Fiber	Omega-3 Oils	Probiotics	Enzymes
Breakfast	amount				
Snacks:					
Breakfast Totals:					
Lunch	amount				
Snacks:					
Lunch Totals:					
Dinner	amount				
Snacks:					
Dinner Totals:					

Supplements

Description:	High Fiber	Oils	Probiotics	Enzymes

TODAY'S GRAND TOTALS

High Fiber	Probiotics

Oils	Enzymes

8 oz. glasses of water consumed

☐ ☐ ☐ ☐ ☐ ☐ ☐ ☐
☐ ☐ ☐ ☐ ☐ ☐ ☐ ☐

Notes:

H.O.P.E. Daily Goal - High Fiber : 35g. - Oils : 2g. - Probiotics : At least 6 Billion Cultures - Enzymes: with each Meal

Date:	Day #:		Day of the week:		

FOOD		High Fiber	Omega-3 Oils	Probiotics	Enzymes
Breakfast	amount				
Snacks:					
Breakfast Totals:					
Lunch	amount				
Snacks:					
Lunch Totals:					
Dinner	amount				
Snacks:					
Dinner Totals:					

Supplements				
Description:	High Fiber	Oils	Probiotics	Enzymes

TODAY'S GRAND TOTALS

High Fiber	Probiotics
Oils	Enzymes

8 oz. glasses of water consumed

☐☐☐☐☐☐☐☐
☐☐☐☐☐☐☐☐

Notes:

H.O.P.E. Daily Goal - High Fiber : 35g. - Oils : 2g. - Probiotics : At least 6 Billion Cultures - Enzymes: with each Meal

Date:	Day #:		Day of the week:

FOOD		High Fiber	Omega-3 Oils	Probiotics	Enzymes

Breakfast   amount

Snacks:					
Breakfast Totals:					

Lunch   amount

Snacks:					
Lunch Totals:					

Dinner   amount

Snacks:					
Dinner Totals:					

Supplements

Description:	High Fiber	Oils	Probiotics	Enzymes

TODAY'S GRAND TOTALS

High Fiber	Probiotics
Oils	Enzymes

8 oz. glasses of water consumed

☐☐☐☐☐☐☐
☐☐☐☐☐☐☐

Notes:

Date:	Day #:		Day of the week:	

FOOD		High Fiber	Omega-3 Oils	Probiotics	Enzymes

Breakfast — amount

Snacks:					
Breakfast Totals:					

Lunch — amount

Snacks:					
Lunch Totals:					

Dinner — amount

Snacks:					
Dinner Totals:					

Supplements

Description:	High Fiber	Oils	Probiotics	Enzymes

TODAY'S GRAND TOTALS

High Fiber	Probiotics
Oils	Enzymes

8 oz. glasses of water consumed

☐ ☐ ☐ ☐ ☐ ☐ ☐
☐ ☐ ☐ ☐ ☐ ☐ ☐

Notes:

H.O.P.E. Daily Goal - High Fiber : 35g. - Oils : 2g. - Probiotics : At least 6 Billion Cultures - Enzymes: with each Meal

Date: Day #:   Day of the week:

FOOD	High Fiber	Omega-3 Oils	Probiotics	Enzymes
Breakfast amount				
Snacks:				
Breakfast Totals:				
Lunch amount				
Snacks:				
Lunch Totals:				
Dinner amount				
Snacks:				
Dinner Totals:				

Supplements

Description:	High Fiber	Oils	Probiotics	Enzymes

TODAY'S GRAND TOTALS

High Fiber	Probiotics
Oils	Enzymes

8 oz. glasses of water consumed

☐☐☐☐☐☐☐☐
☐☐☐☐☐☐☐☐

Notes:

H.O.P.E. Daily Goal - High Fiber : 35g. - Oils : 2g. - Probiotics : At least 6 Billion Cultures - Enzymes: with each Meal

Date:	Day #:		Day of the week:

FOOD	High Fiber	Omega-3 Oils	Probiotics	Enzymes
Breakfast amount				
Snacks:				
Breakfast Totals:				
Lunch amount				
Snacks:				
Lunch Totals:				
Dinner amount				
Snacks:				
Dinner Totals:				

Supplements

Description:	High Fiber	Oils	Probiotics	Enzymes

TODAY'S GRAND TOTALS

High Fiber	Probiotics
Oils	Enzymes

8 oz. glasses of water consumed

☐☐☐☐☐☐☐☐
☐☐☐☐☐☐☐☐

Notes:

H.O.P.E. Daily Goal - High Fiber : 35g. - Oils : 2g. - Probiotics : At least 6 Billion Cultures - Enzymes: with each Meal

Date:	Day #:		Day of the week:

FOOD	High Fiber	Omega-3 Oils	Probiotics	Enzymes
Breakfast amount				
Snacks:				
Breakfast Totals:				
Lunch amount				
Snacks:				
Lunch Totals:				
Dinner amount				
Snacks:				
Dinner Totals:				

Supplements				
Description:	High Fiber	Oils	Probiotics	Enzymes

TODAY'S GRAND TOTALS

High Fiber	Probiotics

Oils	Enzymes

8 oz. glasses of water consumed

☐ ☐ ☐ ☐ ☐ ☐ ☐ ☐
☐ ☐ ☐ ☐ ☐ ☐ ☐ ☐

Notes:

H.O.P.E. Daily Goal - High Fiber : 35g. - Oils : 2g. - Probiotics : At least 6 Billion Cultures - Enzymes: with each Meal

Date:	Day #:		Day of the week:

FOOD	High Fiber	Omega-3 Oils	Probiotics	Enzymes

Breakfast	amount				
Snacks:					
Breakfast Totals:					

Lunch	amount				
Snacks:					
Lunch Totals:					

Dinner	amount				
Snacks:					
Dinner Totals:					

Supplements				
Description:	High Fiber	Oils	Probiotics	Enzymes

TODAY'S GRAND TOTALS

High Fiber	Probiotics
Oils	Enzymes

8 oz. glasses of water consumed
☐☐☐☐☐☐☐☐
☐☐☐☐☐☐☐☐

Notes:

H.O.P.E. Daily Goal - High Fiber : 35g. - Oils : 2g. - Probiotics : At least 6 Billion Cultures - Enzymes : with each Meal

Date:	Day #:	Day of the week:

FOOD	High Fiber	Omega-3 Oils	Probiotics	Enzymes
Breakfast amount				
Snacks:				
Breakfast Totals:				
Lunch amount				
Snacks:				
Lunch Totals:				
Dinner amount				
Snacks:				
Dinner Totals:				

Supplements

Description:	High Fiber	Oils	Probiotics	Enzymes

TODAY'S GRAND TOTALS

High Fiber	Probiotics
Oils	Enzymes

8 oz. glasses of water consumed

☐ ☐ ☐ ☐ ☐ ☐ ☐ ☐
☐ ☐ ☐ ☐ ☐ ☐ ☐ ☐

Notes:

Date:		Day #:		Day of the week:		

FOOD		High Fiber	Omega-3 Oils	Probiotics	Enzymes
Breakfast	amount				
Snacks:					
Breakfast Totals:					
Lunch	amount				
Snacks:					
Lunch Totals:					
Dinner	amount				
Snacks:					
Dinner Totals:					

Supplements

Description:	High Fiber	Oils	Probiotics	Enzymes

TODAY'S GRAND TOTALS

High Fiber	Probiotics
Oils	Enzymes

8 oz. glasses of water consumed

☐☐☐☐☐☐☐☐
☐☐☐☐☐☐☐☐

Notes:

H.O.P.E. Daily Goal - High Fiber : 35g. - Oils : 2g. - Probiotics : At least 6 Billion Cultures - Enzymes: with each Meal

Date:	Day #:	Day of the week:

FOOD	High Fiber	Omega-3 Oils	Probiotics	Enzymes

Breakfast — amount

Snacks:				
Breakfast Totals:				

Lunch — amount

Snacks:				
Lunch Totals:				

Dinner — amount

Snacks:				
Dinner Totals:				

Supplements

Description:	High Fiber	Oils	Probiotics	Enzymes

TODAY'S GRAND TOTALS

High Fiber	Probiotics

Oils	Enzymes

8 oz. glasses of water consumed

□ □ □ □ □ □ □
□ □ □ □ □ □ □

Notes:

Date: _____ Day #: _____ Day of the week: _____

FOOD	High Fiber	Omega-3 Oils	Probiotics	Enzymes

Breakfast amount

Snacks:				
Breakfast Totals:				

Lunch amount

Snacks:				
Lunch Totals:				

Dinner amount

Snacks:				
Dinner Totals:				

Supplements

Description:	High Fiber	Oils	Probiotics	Enzymes

TODAY'S GRAND TOTALS

High Fiber	Probiotics
Oils	Enzymes

8 oz. glasses of water consumed

☐☐☐☐☐☐☐☐
☐☐☐☐☐☐☐☐

Notes:

H.O.P.E. Daily Goal - High Fiber : 35g. - Oils : 2g. - Probiotics : At least 6 Billion Cultures - Enzymes: with each Meal

Date:	Day #:		Day of the week:

FOOD	amount	High Fiber	Omega-3 Oils	Probiotics	Enzymes

Breakfast *amount*

Snacks:					
Breakfast Totals:					

Lunch *amount*

Snacks:					
Lunch Totals:					

Dinner *amount*

Snacks:					
Dinner Totals:					

Supplements

Description:	High Fiber	Oils	Probiotics	Enzymes

TODAY'S GRAND TOTALS

High Fiber	Probiotics

Oils	Enzymes

8 oz. glasses of water consumed

Notes:

Date:	Day #:		Day of the week:

FOOD

		High Fiber	Omega-3 Oils	Probiotics	Enzymes

Breakfast — amount

Snacks:					
Breakfast Totals:					

Lunch — amount

Snacks:					
Lunch Totals:					

Dinner — amount

Snacks:					
Dinner Totals:					

Supplements

Description:	High Fiber	Oils	Probiotics	Enzymes

TODAY'S GRAND TOTALS

High Fiber	Probiotics
Oils	Enzymes

8 oz. glasses of water consumed

☐ ☐ ☐ ☐ ☐ ☐ ☐ ☐
☐ ☐ ☐ ☐ ☐ ☐ ☐ ☐

Notes:

H.O.P.E. Daily Goal - High Fiber : 35g. - Oils : 2g. - Probiotics : At least 6 Billion Cultures - Enzymes: with each Meal

Date:	Day #:	Day of the week:

FOOD	High Fiber	Omega-3 Oils	Probiotics	Enzymes

Breakfast — amount

Snacks:				
Breakfast Totals:				

Lunch — amount

Snacks:				
Lunch Totals:				

Dinner — amount

Snacks:				
Dinner Totals:				

Supplements

Description:	High Fiber	Oils	Probiotics	Enzymes

TODAY'S GRAND TOTALS

High Fiber	Probiotics
Oils	Enzymes

8 oz. glasses of water consumed

☐☐☐☐☐☐☐☐
☐☐☐☐☐☐☐☐

Notes:

H.O.P.E. Daily Goal - High Fiber : 35g. - Oils : 2g. - Probiotics : At least 6 Billion Cultures - Enzymes : with each Med

| Date: | Day #: | | Day of the week: | | | |

FOOD		High Fiber	Omega-3 Oils	Probiotics	Enzymes
Breakfast amount					
Snacks:					
Breakfast Totals:					
Lunch amount					
Snacks:					
Lunch Totals:					
Dinner amount					
Snacks:					
Dinner Totals:					

Supplements

Description:	High Fiber	Oils	Probiotics	Enzymes

TODAY'S GRAND TOTALS

High Fiber	Probiotics
Oils	Enzymes

8 oz. glasses of water consumed
☐☐☐☐☐☐☐☐
☐☐☐☐☐☐☐☐

Notes:

H.O.P.E. Daily Goal - High Fiber : 35g. - Oils : 2g. - Probiotics : At least 6 Billion Cultures - Enzymes: with each Meal

Date:	Day #:	Day of the week:

FOOD	High Fiber	Omega-3 Oils	Probiotics	Enzymes
Breakfast amount				
Snacks:				
Breakfast Totals:				
Lunch amount				
Snacks:				
Lunch Totals:				
Dinner amount				
Snacks:				
Dinner Totals:				

Supplements

Description:	High Fiber	Oils	Probiotics	Enzymes

TODAY'S GRAND TOTALS

High Fiber	Probiotics
Oils	Enzymes

8 oz. glasses of water consumed

☐☐☐☐☐☐☐☐
☐☐☐☐☐☐☐☐

Notes:

Date:		Day #:		Day of the week:	

FOOD		High Fiber	Omega-3 Oils	Probiotics	Enzymes

Breakfast	amount				
Snacks:					
Breakfast Totals:					

Lunch	amount				
Snacks:					
Lunch Totals:					

Dinner	amount				
Snacks:					
Dinner Totals:					

Supplements

Description:	High Fiber	Oils	Probiotics	Enzymes

TODAY'S GRAND TOTALS

High Fiber	Probiotics
Oils	Enzymes

8 oz. glasses of water consumed

☐☐☐☐☐☐☐☐
☐☐☐☐☐☐☐☐

Notes:

H.O.P.E. Daily Goal - High Fiber : 35g. - Oils : 2g. - Probiotics : At least 6 Billion Cultures - Enzymes: with each Meal

Date:	Day #:	Day of the week:

FOOD		High Fiber	Omega-3 Oils	Probiotics	Enzymes
Breakfast	amount				
Snacks:					
Breakfast Totals:					
Lunch	amount				
Snacks:					
Lunch Totals:					
Dinner	amount				
Snacks:					
Dinner Totals:					

Supplements					
Description:	High Fiber	Oils	Probiotics	Enzymes	

TODAY'S GRAND TOTALS

High Fiber	Probiotics
Oils	Enzymes

8 oz. glasses of water consumed

☐☐☐☐☐☐☐☐
☐☐☐☐☐☐☐☐

Notes:

Date: _____ Day #: _____ Day of the week: _____

FOOD	High Fiber	Omega-3 Oils	Probiotics	Enzymes
Breakfast amount				
Snacks:				
Breakfast Totals:				
Lunch amount				
Snacks:				
Lunch Totals:				
Dinner amount				
Snacks:				
Dinner Totals:				

Supplements

Description:	High Fiber	Oils	Probiotics	Enzymes

TODAY'S GRAND TOTALS

High Fiber	Probiotics
Oils	Enzymes

8 oz. glasses of water consumed

☐ ☐ ☐ ☐ ☐ ☐ ☐
☐ ☐ ☐ ☐ ☐ ☐ ☐

Notes:

H.O.P.E. Daily Goal - High Fiber : 35g. - Oils : 2g. - Probiotics : At least 6 Billion Cultures - Enzymes: with each Meal

Date:	Day #:	Day of the week:

FOOD	High Fiber	Omega-3 Oils	Probiotics	Enzymes

Breakfast — amount

Snacks:				
Breakfast Totals:				

Lunch — amount

Snacks:				
Lunch Totals:				

Dinner — amount

Snacks:				
Dinner Totals:				

Supplements

Description:	High Fiber	Oils	Probiotics	Enzymes

TODAY'S GRAND TOTALS

High Fiber	Probiotics
Oils	Enzymes

8 oz. glasses of water consumed

☐ ☐ ☐ ☐ ☐ ☐ ☐ ☐
☐ ☐ ☐ ☐ ☐ ☐ ☐ ☐

Notes:

H.O.P.E. Daily Goal - High Fiber : 35g. - Oils : 2g. - Probiotics : At least 6 Billion Cultures - Enzymes: with each Meal

| Date: | Day #: | | Day of the week: |

FOOD		High Fiber	Omega-3 Oils	Probiotics	Enzymes
Breakfast	amount				
Snacks:					
Breakfast Totals:					
Lunch	amount				
Snacks:					
Lunch Totals:					
Dinner	amount				
Snacks:					
Dinner Totals:					

Supplements

Description:	High Fiber	Oils	Probiotics	Enzymes

TODAY'S GRAND TOTALS

High Fiber	Probiotics
Oils	Enzymes

8 oz. glasses of water consumed

☐☐☐☐☐☐☐☐
☐☐☐☐☐☐☐☐

Notes:

H.O.P.E. Daily Goal - High Fiber : 35g. - Oils : 2g. - Probiotics : At least 6 Billion Cultures - Enzymes : with each Meal

Date:	Day #:	Day of the week:

FOOD	High Fiber	Omega-3 Oils	Probiotics	Enzymes

Breakfast — amount

Snacks:				
Breakfast Totals:				

Lunch — amount

Snacks:				
Lunch Totals:				

Dinner — amount

Snacks:				
Dinner Totals:				

Supplements

Description:	High Fiber	Oils	Probiotics	Enzymes

TODAY'S GRAND TOTALS

High Fiber	Probiotics
Oils	Enzymes

8 oz. glasses of water consumed

☐☐☐☐☐☐☐
☐☐☐☐☐☐☐

Notes:

Date: _____ Day #: _____ Day of the week: _____

FOOD	High Fiber	Omega-3 Oils	Probiotics	Enzymes
Breakfast amount				
Snacks:				
Breakfast Totals:				
Lunch amount				
Snacks:				
Lunch Totals:				
Dinner amount				
Snacks:				
Dinner Totals:				

Supplements

Description:	High Fiber	Oils	Probiotics	Enzymes

TODAY'S GRAND TOTALS

High Fiber	Probiotics
Oils	Enzymes

8 oz. glasses of water consumed
☐☐☐☐☐☐☐
☐☐☐☐☐☐☐☐

Notes:

H.O.P.E. Daily Goal - High Fiber : 35g. - Oils : 2g. - Probiotics : At least 6 Billion Cultures - Enzymes : with each Meal

Date:	Day #:	Day of the week:

FOOD		High Fiber	Omega-3 Oils	Probiotics	Enzymes

Breakfast — amount

Snacks:					
Breakfast Totals:					

Lunch — amount

Snacks:					
Lunch Totals:					

Dinner — amount

Snacks:					
Dinner Totals:					

Supplements

Description:	High Fiber	Oils	Probiotics	Enzymes

TODAY'S GRAND TOTALS

High Fiber	Probiotics
Oils	Enzymes

8 oz. glasses of water consumed

☐☐☐☐☐☐☐☐
☐☐☐☐☐☐☐☐

Notes:

Date:	Day #:	Day of the week:

FOOD		High Fiber	Omega-3 Oils	Probiotics	Enzymes

Breakfast   amount

Snacks:					
Breakfast Totals:					

Lunch   amount

Snacks:					
Lunch Totals:					

Dinner   amount

Snacks:					
Dinner Totals:					

Supplements

Description:	High Fiber	Oils	Probiotics	Enzymes

TODAY'S GRAND TOTALS

High Fiber	Probiotics
Oils	Enzymes

8 oz. glasses of water consumed

☐☐☐☐☐☐☐☐
☐☐☐☐☐☐☐☐

Notes:

H.O.P.E. Daily Goal - High Fiber : 35g. - Oils : 2g. - Probiotics : At least 6 Billion Cultures - Enzymes: with each Meal

Date:	Day #:	Day of the week:

FOOD		High Fiber	Omega-3 Oils	Probiotics	Enzymes
Breakfast	amount				
Snacks:					
Breakfast Totals:					
Lunch	amount				
Snacks:					
Lunch Totals:					
Dinner	amount				
Snacks:					
Dinner Totals:					

Supplements

Description:	High Fiber	Oils	Probiotics	Enzymes

TODAY'S GRAND TOTALS

High Fiber	Probiotics
Oils	Enzymes

8 oz. glasses of water consumed

☐☐☐☐☐☐☐☐
☐☐☐☐☐☐☐☐

Notes:

| Date: | Day #: | | Day of the week: | | |

FOOD		High Fiber	Omega-3 Oils	Probiotics	Enzymes
Breakfast	amount				
Snacks:					
Breakfast Totals:					
Lunch	amount				
Snacks:					
Lunch Totals:					
Dinner	amount				
Snacks:					
Dinner Totals:					

Supplements

Description:	High Fiber	Oils	Probiotics	Enzymes

TODAY'S GRAND TOTALS

High Fiber	Probiotics

Oils	Enzymes

8 oz. glasses of water consumed

☐☐☐☐☐☐☐
☐☐☐☐☐☐☐

Notes:

Date:	Day #:	Day of the week:

FOOD		High Fiber	Omega-3 Oils	Probiotics	Enzymes

Breakfast   amount

Snacks:					
Breakfast Totals:					

Lunch   amount

Snacks:					
Lunch Totals:					

Dinner   amount

Snacks:					
Dinner Totals:					

Supplements

Description:	High Fiber	Oils	Probiotics	Enzymes

TODAY'S GRAND TOTALS

High Fiber	Probiotics
Oils	Enzymes

8 oz. glasses of water consumed

☐ ☐ ☐ ☐ ☐ ☐ ☐
☐ ☐ ☐ ☐ ☐ ☐ ☐

Notes:

Date:	Day #:	Day of the week:

FOOD		High Fiber	Omega-3 Oils	Probiotics	Enzymes

Breakfast   amount

Snacks:					
Breakfast Totals:					

Lunch   amount

Snacks:					
Lunch Totals:					

Dinner   amount

Snacks:					
Dinner Totals:					

Supplements

Description:	High Fiber	Oils	Probiotics	Enzymes

TODAY'S GRAND TOTALS

High Fiber	Probiotics
Oils	Enzymes

8 oz. glasses of water consumed

☐☐☐☐☐☐☐☐
☐☐☐☐☐☐☐☐

Notes:

H.O.P.E. Daily Goal - High Fiber : 35g. - Oils : 2g. - Probiotics : At least 6 Billion Cultures - Enzymes: with each Meal

Date:	Day #:	Day of the week:

FOOD	High Fiber	Omega-3 Oils	Probiotics	Enzymes

Breakfast   amount

Snacks:				
Breakfast Totals:				

Lunch   amount

Snacks:				
Lunch Totals:				

Dinner   amount

Snacks:				
Dinner Totals:				

Supplements

Description:	High Fiber	Oils	Probiotics	Enzymes

TODAY'S GRAND TOTALS

High Fiber	Probiotics
Oils	Enzymes

8 oz. glasses of water consumed
☐☐☐☐☐☐☐☐
☐☐☐☐☐☐☐☐

Notes:

Date:	Day # :	Day of the week:

FOOD		High Fiber	Omega-3 Oils	Probiotics	Enzymes

Breakfast — amount

Snacks:					
Breakfast Totals:					

Lunch — amount

Snacks:					
Lunch Totals:					

Dinner — amount

Snacks:					
Dinner Totals:					

Supplements

Description:	High Fiber	Oils	Probiotics	Enzymes

TODAY'S GRAND TOTALS

High Fiber	Probiotics
Oils	Enzymes

8 oz. glasses of water consumed

☐☐☐☐☐☐☐
☐☐☐☐☐☐☐

Notes:

H.O.P.E. Daily Goal - High Fiber : 35g. - Oils : 2g. - Probiotics : At least 6 Billion Cultures - Enzymes: with each Meal

Date:	Day #:		Day of the week:

FOOD		High Fiber	Omega-3 Oils	Probiotics	Enzymes
Breakfast	amount				
Snacks:					
Breakfast Totals:					
Lunch	amount				
Snacks:					
Lunch Totals:					
Dinner	amount				
Snacks:					
Dinner Totals:					

Supplements

Description:	High Fiber	Oils	Probiotics	Enzymes

TODAY'S GRAND TOTALS

High Fiber	Probiotics
Oils	Enzymes

8 oz. glasses of water consumed

☐☐☐☐☐☐☐
☐☐☐☐☐☐☐

Notes:

H.O.P.E. Daily Goal - High Fiber : 35g. - Oils : 2g. - Probiotics : At least 6 Billion Cultures - Enzymes: with each Mea

| Date: | Day #: | | Day of the week: |

FOOD		High Fiber	Omega-3 Oils	Probiotics	Enzymes
Breakfast	amount				
Snacks:					
Breakfast Totals:					
Lunch	amount				
Snacks:					
Lunch Totals:					
Dinner	amount				
Snacks:					
Dinner Totals:					

Supplements

Description:	High Fiber	Oils	Probiotics	Enzymes

TODAY'S GRAND TOTALS

High Fiber	Probiotics
Oils	Enzymes

8 oz. glasses of water consumed

☐☐☐☐☐☐☐
☐☐☐☐☐☐☐

Notes:

H.O.P.E. Daily Goal - High Fiber : 35g. - Oils : 2g. - Probiotics : At least 6 Billion Cultures - Enzymes: with each Meal

Date:	Day #:	Day of the week:

FOOD		High Fiber	Omega-3 Oils	Probiotics	Enzymes
Breakfast	amount				
Snacks:					
Breakfast Totals:					
Lunch	amount				
Snacks:					
Lunch Totals:					
Dinner	amount				
Snacks:					
Dinner Totals:					

Supplements

Description:	High Fiber	Oils	Probiotics	Enzymes

TODAY'S GRAND TOTALS

High Fiber	Probiotics
Oils	Enzymes

8 oz. glasses of water consumed

☐☐☐☐☐☐☐
☐☐☐☐☐☐☐

Notes:

H.O.P.E. Daily Goal - High Fiber : 35g. - Oils : 2g. - Probiotics : At least 6 Billion Cultures - Enzymes: with each Meal

Date:	Day #:		Day of the week:		

FOOD		High Fiber	Omega-3 Oils	Probiotics	Enzymes
Breakfast	amount				
Snacks:					
Breakfast Totals:					
Lunch	amount				
Snacks:					
Lunch Totals:					
Dinner	amount				
Snacks:					
Dinner Totals:					

Supplements				
Description:	High Fiber	Oils	Probiotics	Enzymes

TODAY'S GRAND TOTALS

High Fiber	Probiotics
Oils	Enzymes

8 oz. glasses of water consumed

☐☐☐☐☐☐☐☐
☐☐☐☐☐☐☐☐

Notes:

H.O.P.E. Daily Goal - High Fiber : 35g. - Oils : 2g. - Probiotics : At least 6 Billion Cultures - Enzymes: with each Meal

Date:	Day #:	Day of the week:

FOOD		High Fiber	Omega-3 Oils	Probiotics	Enzymes
Breakfast	amount				
Snacks:					
Breakfast Totals:					
Lunch	amount				
Snacks:					
Lunch Totals:					
Dinner	amount				
Snacks:					
Dinner Totals:					

Supplements

Description:	High Fiber	Oils	Probiotics	Enzymes

TODAY'S GRAND TOTALS

High Fiber	Probiotics
Oils	Enzymes

8 oz. glasses of water consumed

☐☐☐☐☐☐☐☐
☐☐☐☐☐☐☐☐

Notes:

H.O.P.E. Daily Goal - High Fiber : 35g. - Oils : 2g. - Probiotics : At least 6 Billion Cultures - Enzymes: with each Meal

Date:	Day #:		Day of the week:		

FOOD		High Fiber	Omega-3 Oils	Probiotics	Enzymes
Breakfast	amount				
Snacks:					
Breakfast Totals:					
Lunch	amount				
Snacks:					
Lunch Totals:					
Dinner	amount				
Snacks:					
Dinner Totals:					

Supplements

Description:	High Fiber	Oils	Probiotics	Enzymes

TODAY'S GRAND TOTALS

High Fiber	Probiotics
Oils	Enzymes

8 oz. glasses of water consumed

☐ ☐ ☐ ☐ ☐ ☐ ☐ ☐
☐ ☐ ☐ ☐ ☐ ☐ ☐ ☐

Notes:

H.O.P.E. Daily Goal - High Fiber : 35g. - Oils : 2g. - Probiotics : At least 6 Billion Cultures - Enzymes: with each Meal

Date:	Day #:	Day of the week:

FOOD	High Fiber	Omega-3 Oils	Probiotics	Enzymes

Breakfast — amount

	High Fiber	Omega-3 Oils	Probiotics	Enzymes
Snacks:				
Breakfast Totals:				

Lunch — amount

	High Fiber	Omega-3 Oils	Probiotics	Enzymes
Snacks:				
Lunch Totals:				

Dinner — amount

	High Fiber	Omega-3 Oils	Probiotics	Enzymes
Snacks:				
Dinner Totals:				

Supplements

Description:	High Fiber	Oils	Probiotics	Enzymes

TODAY'S GRAND TOTALS

High Fiber	Probiotics
Oils	Enzymes

8 oz. glasses of water consumed

☐☐☐☐☐☐☐
☐☐☐☐☐☐☐

Notes:

H.O.P.E. Daily Goal - High Fiber : 35g. - Oils : 2g. - Probiotics : At least 6 Billion Cultures - Enzymes : with each Meal

Date:	Day #:		Day of the week:

FOOD	High Fiber	Omega-3 Oils	Probiotics	Enzymes

Breakfast — amount

	High Fiber	Omega-3 Oils	Probiotics	Enzymes
Snacks:				
Breakfast Totals:				

Lunch — amount

	High Fiber	Omega-3 Oils	Probiotics	Enzymes
Snacks:				
Lunch Totals:				

Dinner — amount

	High Fiber	Omega-3 Oils	Probiotics	Enzymes
Snacks:				
Dinner Totals:				

Supplements

Description:	High Fiber	Oils	Probiotics	Enzymes

TODAY'S GRAND TOTALS

High Fiber	Probiotics
Oils	Enzymes

8 oz. glasses of water consumed

☐ ☐ ☐ ☐ ☐ ☐ ☐ ☐
☐ ☐ ☐ ☐ ☐ ☐ ☐ ☐

Notes:

H.O.P.E. Daily Goal - High Fiber : 35g. - Oils : 2g. - Probiotics : At least 6 Billion Cultures - Enzymes: with each Meal

Date:	Day #:	Day of the week:

FOOD		High Fiber	Omega-3 Oils	Probiotics	Enzymes

Breakfast amount

Snacks:					
Breakfast Totals:					

Lunch amount

Snacks:					
Lunch Totals:					

Dinner amount

Snacks:					
Dinner Totals:					

Supplements

Description:	High Fiber	Oils	Probiotics	Enzymes

TODAY'S GRAND TOTALS

High Fiber	Probiotics
Oils	Enzymes

8 oz. glasses of water consumed

☐☐☐☐☐☐☐☐
☐☐☐☐☐☐☐☐

Notes:

H.O.P.E. Daily Goal - High Fiber : 35g. - Oils : 2g. - Probiotics : At least 6 Billion Cultures - Enzymes : with each Meal

Date:	Day #:	Day of the week:

FOOD	High Fiber	Omega-3 Oils	Probiotics	Enzymes

Breakfast — amount

Snacks:				
Breakfast Totals:				

Lunch — amount

Snacks:				
Lunch Totals:				

Dinner — amount

Snacks:				
Dinner Totals:				

Supplements

Description:	High Fiber	Oils	Probiotics	Enzymes

TODAY'S GRAND TOTALS

High Fiber	Probiotics
Oils	Enzymes

8 oz. glasses of water consumed

☐ ☐ ☐ ☐ ☐ ☐ ☐ ☐
☐ ☐ ☐ ☐ ☐ ☐ ☐ ☐

Notes:

H.O.P.E. Daily Goal - High Fiber : 35g. - Oils : 2g. - Probiotics : At least 6 Billion Cultures - Enzymes: with each Meal

Date:	Day #:	Day of the week:

FOOD	High Fiber	Omega-3 Oils	Probiotics	Enzymes
Breakfast amount				
Snacks:				
Breakfast Totals:				
Lunch amount				
Snacks:				
Lunch Totals:				
Dinner amount				
Snacks:				
Dinner Totals:				

Supplements				
Description:	High Fiber	Oils	Probiotics	Enzymes

TODAY'S GRAND TOTALS

High Fiber	Probiotics
Oils	Enzymes

8 oz. glasses of water consumed
☐☐☐☐☐☐☐☐
☐☐☐☐☐☐☐☐

Notes:

H.O.P.E. Daily Goal - High Fiber : 35g. - Oils : 2g. - Probiotics : At least 6 Billion Cultures - Enzymes: with each Meal

Date:	Day #:		Day of the week:		

FOOD		High Fiber	Omega-3 Oils	Probiotics	Enzymes
Breakfast	amount				
Snacks:					
Breakfast Totals:					
Lunch	amount				
Snacks:					
Lunch Totals:					
Dinner	amount				
Snacks:					
Dinner Totals:					

Supplements

Description:	High Fiber	Oils	Probiotics	Enzymes

TODAY'S GRAND TOTALS

High Fiber	Probiotics
Oils	Enzymes

8 oz. glasses of water consumed

☐☐☐☐☐☐☐☐
☐☐☐☐☐☐☐☐

Notes:

H.O.P.E. Daily Goal - High Fiber : 35g. - Oils : 2g. - Probiotics : At least 6 Billion Cultures - Enzymes: with each Meal

Date:	Day #:	Day of the week:

FOOD		High Fiber	Omega-3 Oils	Probiotics	Enzymes
Breakfast	amount				
Snacks:					
Breakfast Totals:					
Lunch	amount				
Snacks:					
Lunch Totals:					
Dinner	amount				
Snacks:					
Dinner Totals:					

Supplements					
Description:	High Fiber	Oils	Probiotics	Enzymes	

TODAY'S GRAND TOTALS

High Fiber	Probiotics
Oils	Enzymes

8 oz. glasses of water consumed

☐☐☐☐☐☐☐
☐☐☐☐☐☐☐

Notes:

Date: _____ Day #: _____ Day of the week: _____

FOOD	High Fiber	Omega-3 Oils	Probiotics	Enzymes

Breakfast	amount				
Snacks:					
Breakfast Totals:					

Lunch	amount				
Snacks:					
Lunch Totals:					

Dinner	amount				
Snacks:					
Dinner Totals:					

Supplements

Description:	High Fiber	Oils	Probiotics	Enzymes

TODAY'S GRAND TOTALS

High Fiber	Probiotics
Oils	Enzymes

8 oz. glasses of water consumed

☐☐☐☐☐☐☐☐
☐☐☐☐☐☐☐☐

Notes:

H.O.P.E. Daily Goal - High Fiber : 35g. - Oils : 2g. - Probiotics : At least 6 Billion Cultures - Enzymes: with each Meal

Date:	Day #:	Day of the week:

FOOD		High Fiber	Omega-3 Oils	Probiotics	Enzymes
Breakfast	amount				
Snacks:					
Breakfast Totals:					
Lunch	amount				
Snacks:					
Lunch Totals:					
Dinner	amount				
Snacks:					
Dinner Totals:					

Supplements					
Description:	High Fiber	Oils	Probiotics	Enzymes	

TODAY'S GRAND TOTALS

High Fiber	Probiotics
Oils	Enzymes

8 oz. glasses of water consumed

☐☐☐☐☐☐☐
☐☐☐☐☐☐☐

Notes:

Date:		Day #:		Day of the week:	

FOOD		High Fiber	Omega-3 Oils	Probiotics	Enzymes
Breakfast	amount				
Snacks:					
Breakfast Totals:					

Lunch	amount				
Snacks:					
Lunch Totals:					

Dinner	amount				
Snacks:					
Dinner Totals:					

Supplements

Description:	High Fiber	Oils	Probiotics	Enzymes

TODAY'S GRAND TOTALS

High Fiber	Probiotics
Oils	Enzymes

8 oz. glasses of water consumed

☐ ☐ ☐ ☐ ☐ ☐ ☐ ☐
☐ ☐ ☐ ☐ ☐ ☐ ☐ ☐

Notes:

H.O.P.E. Daily Goal - High Fiber : 35g. - Oils : 2g. - Probiotics : At least 6 Billion Cultures - Enzymes: with each Meal

Date:	Day #:	Day of the week:

FOOD	High Fiber	Omega-3 Oils	Probiotics	Enzymes

Breakfast — amount

Snacks:				
Breakfast Totals:				

Lunch — amount

Snacks:				
Lunch Totals:				

Dinner — amount

Snacks:				
Dinner Totals:				

Supplements

Description:	High Fiber	Oils	Probiotics	Enzymes

TODAY'S GRAND TOTALS

High Fiber	Probiotics
Oils	Enzymes

8 oz. glasses of water consumed

☐☐☐☐☐☐☐
☐☐☐☐☐☐☐

Notes:

Date: Day #:   Day of the week:

FOOD		High Fiber	Omega-3 Oils	Probiotics	Enzymes
Breakfast	amount				
Snacks:					
Breakfast Totals:					
Lunch	amount				
Snacks:					
Lunch Totals:					
Dinner	amount				
Snacks:					
Dinner Totals:					

Supplements

Description:	High Fiber	Oils	Probiotics	Enzymes

TODAY'S GRAND TOTALS

High Fiber	Probiotics
Oils	Enzymes

8 oz. glasses of water consumed

☐☐☐☐☐☐☐☐
☐☐☐☐☐☐☐☐

Notes:

H.O.P.E. Daily Goal - High Fiber : 35g. - Oils : 2g. - Probiotics : At least 6 Billion Cultures - Enzymes: with each Meal

Date:	Day #:	Day of the week:

FOOD	High Fiber	Omega-3 Oils	Probiotics	Enzymes

Breakfast — amount

Snacks:				
Breakfast Totals:				

Lunch — amount

Snacks:				
Lunch Totals:				

Dinner — amount

Snacks:				
Dinner Totals:				

Supplements

Description:	High Fiber	Oils	Probiotics	Enzymes

TODAY'S GRAND TOTALS

High Fiber	Probiotics
Oils	Enzymes

8 oz. glasses of water consumed
☐ ☐ ☐ ☐ ☐ ☐ ☐ ☐
☐ ☐ ☐ ☐ ☐ ☐ ☐ ☐

Notes:

Date:	Day #:		Day of the week:		

FOOD		High Fiber	Omega-3 Oils	Probiotics	Enzymes

Breakfast   amount

Snacks:					
Breakfast Totals:					

Lunch   amount

Snacks:					
Lunch Totals:					

Dinner   amount

Snacks:					
Dinner Totals:					

Supplements

Description:	High Fiber	Oils	Probiotics	Enzymes

TODAY'S GRAND TOTALS

High Fiber	Probiotics
Oils	Enzymes

8 oz. glasses of water consumed

☐ ☐ ☐ ☐ ☐ ☐ ☐ ☐ ☐
☐ ☐ ☐ ☐ ☐ ☐ ☐ ☐

Notes:

H.O.P.E. Daily Goal - High Fiber : 35g. - Oils : 2g. - Probiotics : At least 6 Billion Cultures - Enzymes : with each Meal

Date:	Day #:	Day of the week:

FOOD	High Fiber	Omega-3 Oils	Probiotics	Enzymes
Breakfast amount				
Snacks:				
Breakfast Totals:				
Lunch amount				
Snacks:				
Lunch Totals:				
Dinner amount				
Snacks:				
Dinner Totals:				

Supplements				
Description:	High Fiber	Oils	Probiotics	Enzymes

TODAY'S GRAND TOTALS

High Fiber	Probiotics
Oils	Enzymes

8 oz. glasses of water consumed

☐☐☐☐☐☐☐☐
☐☐☐☐☐☐☐☐

Notes:

H.O.P.E. Daily Goal - High Fiber : 35g. - Oils : 2g. - Probiotics : At least 6 Billion Cultures - Enzymes: with each Meal

Date: _____ Day #: _____ Day of the week: _____

FOOD	High Fiber	Omega-3 Oils	Probiotics	Enzymes
Breakfast amount				
Snacks:				
Breakfast Totals:				
Lunch amount				
Snacks:				
Lunch Totals:				
Dinner amount				
Snacks:				
Dinner Totals:				

Supplements

Description:	High Fiber	Oils	Probiotics	Enzymes

TODAY'S GRAND TOTALS

High Fiber	Probiotics

Oils	Enzymes

8 oz. glasses of water consumed
☐☐☐☐☐☐☐☐
☐☐☐☐☐☐☐☐

Notes:

H.O.P.E. Daily Goal - High Fiber : 35g. - Oils : 2g. - Probiotics : At least 6 Billion Cultures - Enzymes: with each Meal

Date:	Day #:		Day of the week:

FOOD		High Fiber	Omega-3 Oils	Probiotics	Enzymes
Breakfast	amount				
Snacks:					
Breakfast Totals:					
Lunch	amount				
Snacks:					
Lunch Totals:					
Dinner	amount				
Snacks:					
Dinner Totals:					

Supplements

Description:	High Fiber	Oils	Probiotics	Enzymes

TODAY'S GRAND TOTALS

High Fiber	Probiotics
Oils	Enzymes

8 oz. glasses of water consumed

☐☐☐☐☐☐☐☐
☐☐☐☐☐☐☐☐

Notes:

H.O.P.E. Daily Goal - High Fiber : 35g. - Oils : 2g. - Probiotics : At least 6 Billion Cultures - Enzymes : with each Meal

Date:	Day #:	Day of the week:

FOOD		High Fiber	Omega-3 Oils	Probiotics	Enzymes
Breakfast	amount				
Snacks:					
Breakfast Totals:					
Lunch	amount				
Snacks:					
Lunch Totals:					
Dinner	amount				
Snacks:					
Dinner Totals:					

Supplements

Description:	High Fiber	Oils	Probiotics	Enzymes

TODAY'S GRAND TOTALS

High Fiber	Probiotics
Oils	Enzymes

8 oz. glasses of water consumed

☐☐☐☐☐☐☐☐
☐☐☐☐☐☐☐☐

Notes:

H.O.P.E. Daily Goal - High Fiber : 35g. - Oils : 2g. - Probiotics : At least 6 Billion Cultures - Enzymes: with each Meal

Date:	Day #:	Day of the week:

FOOD		High Fiber	Omega-3 Oils	Probiotics	Enzymes
Breakfast	amount				
Snacks:					
Breakfast Totals:					
Lunch	amount				
Snacks:					
Lunch Totals:					
Dinner	amount				
Snacks:					
Dinner Totals:					

Supplements

Description:	High Fiber	Oils	Probiotics	Enzymes

TODAY'S GRAND TOTALS

High Fiber	Probiotics
Oils	Enzymes

8 oz. glasses of water consumed

☐ ☐ ☐ ☐ ☐ ☐ ☐ ☐
☐ ☐ ☐ ☐ ☐ ☐ ☐ ☐

Notes:

H.O.P.E. Daily Goal - High Fiber : 35g. - Oils : 2g. - Probiotics : At least 6 Billion Cultures - Enzymes : with each Meal

Date:	Day #:	Day of the week:

FOOD	High Fiber	Omega-3 Oils	Probiotics	Enzymes
Breakfast amount				
Snacks:				
Breakfast Totals:				
Lunch amount				
Snacks:				
Lunch Totals:				
Dinner amount				
Snacks:				
Dinner Totals:				

Supplements

Description:	High Fiber	Oils	Probiotics	Enzymes

TODAY'S GRAND TOTALS

High Fiber	Probiotics
Oils	Enzymes

8 oz. glasses of water consumed
☐☐☐☐☐☐☐
☐☐☐☐☐☐☐

Notes:

H.O.P.E. Daily Goal - High Fiber : 35g. - Oils : 2g. - Probiotics : At least 6 Billion Cultures - Enzymes: with each Meal

Date:	Day #:	Day of the week:

FOOD	High Fiber	Omega-3 Oils	Probiotics	Enzymes

Breakfast amount

	High Fiber	Oils	Probiotics	Enzymes
Snacks:				
Breakfast Totals:				

Lunch amount

	High Fiber	Oils	Probiotics	Enzymes
Snacks:				
Lunch Totals:				

Dinner amount

	High Fiber	Oils	Probiotics	Enzymes
Snacks:				
Dinner Totals:				

Supplements

Description:	High Fiber	Oils	Probiotics	Enzymes

TODAY'S GRAND TOTALS

High Fiber	Probiotics
Oils	Enzymes

8 oz. glasses of water consumed

☐☐☐☐☐☐☐☐
☐☐☐☐☐☐☐☐

Notes:

Date:	Day #:	Day of the week:

FOOD		High Fiber	Omega-3 Oils	Probiotics	Enzymes

Breakfast — amount

	amount				
Snacks:					
Breakfast Totals:					

Lunch — amount

	amount				
Snacks:					
Lunch Totals:					

Dinner — amount

	amount				
Snacks:					
Dinner Totals:					

Supplements

Description:	High Fiber	Oils	Probiotics	Enzymes

TODAY'S GRAND TOTALS

High Fiber	Probiotics
Oils	Enzymes

8 oz. glasses of water consumed

☐ ☐ ☐ ☐ ☐ ☐ ☐ ☐
☐ ☐ ☐ ☐ ☐ ☐ ☐ ☐

Notes:

H.O.P.E. Daily Goal - High Fiber : 35g. - Oils : 2g. - Probiotics : At least 6 Billion Cultures - Enzymes : with each Meal

Date:	Day #:			Day of the week:	

FOOD	High Fiber	Omega-3 Oils	Probiotics	Enzymes

Breakfast   amount

Snacks:				
Breakfast Totals:				

Lunch   amount

Snacks:				
Lunch Totals:				

Dinner   amount

Snacks:				
Dinner Totals:				

Supplements

Description:	High Fiber	Oils	Probiotics	Enzymes

TODAY'S GRAND TOTALS

High Fiber	Probiotics
Oils	Enzymes

8 oz. glasses of water consumed

☐ ☐ ☐ ☐ ☐ ☐ ☐ ☐
☐ ☐ ☐ ☐ ☐ ☐ ☐ ☐

Notes:

Date:		Day #:			Day of the week:		

FOOD		High Fiber	Omega-3 Oils	Probiotics	Enzymes

Breakfast — amount

Snacks:					
Breakfast Totals:					

Lunch — amount

Snacks:					
Lunch Totals:					

Dinner — amount

Snacks:					
Dinner Totals:					

Supplements

Description:	High Fiber	Oils	Probiotics	Enzymes

TODAY'S GRAND TOTALS

High Fiber	Probiotics
Oils	Enzymes

8 oz. glasses of water consumed

☐☐☐☐☐☐☐
☐☐☐☐☐☐☐

Notes:

H.O.P.E. Daily Goal - High Fiber : 35g. - Oils : 2g. - Probiotics : At least 6 Billion Cultures - Enzymes: with each Meal

Date:	Day #:	Day of the week:

FOOD		High Fiber	Omega-3 Oils	Probiotics	Enzymes
Breakfast	amount				
Snacks:					
Breakfast Totals:					
Lunch	amount				
Snacks:					
Lunch Totals:					
Dinner	amount				
Snacks:					
Dinner Totals:					

Supplements					
Description:	High Fiber	Oils	Probiotics	Enzymes	

TODAY'S GRAND TOTALS

High Fiber	Probiotics
Oils	Enzymes

8 oz. glasses of water consumed

☐☐☐☐☐☐☐
☐☐☐☐☐☐☐

Notes:

| Date: | | Day #: | | | Day of the week: | | |

FOOD			High Fiber	Omega-3 Oils	Probiotics	Enzymes

Breakfast   amount

Snacks:					
Breakfast Totals:					

Lunch   amount

Snacks:					
Lunch Totals:					

Dinner   amount

Snacks:					
Dinner Totals:					

Supplements

Description:	High Fiber	Oils	Probiotics	Enzymes

TODAY'S GRAND TOTALS

High Fiber	Probiotics
Oils	Enzymes

8 oz. glasses of water consumed

☐☐☐☐☐☐☐☐
☐☐☐☐☐☐☐☐

Notes:

H.O.P.E. Daily Goal - High Fiber : 35g. - Oils : 2g. - Probiotics : At least 6 Billion Cultures - Enzymes: with each Meal

Date:	Day #:	Day of the week:

FOOD		High Fiber	Omega-3 Oils	Probiotics	Enzymes
Breakfast	amount				
Snacks:					
Breakfast Totals:					
Lunch	amount				
Snacks:					
Lunch Totals:					
Dinner	amount				
Snacks:					
Dinner Totals:					

Supplements

Description:	High Fiber	Oils	Probiotics	Enzymes

TODAY'S GRAND TOTALS

High Fiber	Probiotics

Oils	Enzymes

8 oz. glasses of water consumed

☐☐☐☐☐☐☐
☐☐☐☐☐☐☐

Notes:

| Date: | | Day #: | | Day of the week: | | |

FOOD			High Fiber	Omega-3 Oils	Probiotics	Enzymes
Breakfast		amount				
Snacks:						
Breakfast Totals:						
Lunch		amount				
Snacks:						
Lunch Totals:						
Dinner		amount				
Snacks:						
Dinner Totals:						

Supplements

Description:	High Fiber	Oils	Probiotics	Enzymes

TODAY'S GRAND TOTALS

High Fiber	Probiotics
Oils	Enzymes

8 oz. glasses of water consumed

☐ ☐ ☐ ☐ ☐ ☐ ☐ ☐
☐ ☐ ☐ ☐ ☐ ☐ ☐ ☐

Notes:

H.O.P.E. Daily Goal - High Fiber : 35g. - Oils : 2g. - Probiotics : At least 6 Billion Cultures - Enzymes: with each Meal

Date:	Day #:	Day of the week:

FOOD		High Fiber	Omega-3 Oils	Probiotics	Enzymes
Breakfast	amount				
Snacks:					
Breakfast Totals:					
Lunch	amount				
Snacks:					
Lunch Totals:					
Dinner	amount				
Snacks:					
Dinner Totals:					

Supplements

Description:	High Fiber	Oils	Probiotics	Enzymes

TODAY'S GRAND TOTALS

High Fiber	Probiotics
Oils	Enzymes

8 oz. glasses of water consumed

☐☐☐☐☐☐☐☐
☐☐☐☐☐☐☐☐

Notes:

H.O.P.E. Daily Goal - High Fiber : 35g. - Oils : 2g. - Probiotics : At least 6 Billion Cultures - Enzymes: with each Meal

Date: _____ Day #: _____ Day of the week: _____

FOOD	High Fiber	Omega-3 Oils	Probiotics	Enzymes
Breakfast amount				
Snacks:				
Breakfast Totals:				
Lunch amount				
Snacks:				
Lunch Totals:				
Dinner amount				
Snacks:				
Dinner Totals:				

Supplements

Description:	High Fiber	Oils	Probiotics	Enzymes

TODAY'S GRAND TOTALS

High Fiber	Probiotics
Oils	Enzymes

8 oz. glasses of water consumed
☐☐☐☐☐☐☐☐
☐☐☐☐☐☐☐☐

Notes:

H.O.P.E. Daily Goal - High Fiber : 35g. - Oils : 2g. - Probiotics : At least 6 Billion Cultures - Enzymes: with each Meal

Date:	Day #:	Day of the week:

FOOD		High Fiber	Omega-3 Oils	Probiotics	Enzymes

Breakfast   amount

Snacks:					
Breakfast Totals:					

Lunch   amount

Snacks:					
Lunch Totals:					

Dinner   amount

Snacks:					
Dinner Totals:					

Supplements

Description:	High Fiber	Oils	Probiotics	Enzymes

TODAY'S GRAND TOTALS

High Fiber	Probiotics
Oils	Enzymes

8 oz. glasses of water consumed

☐ ☐ ☐ ☐ ☐ ☐ ☐ ☐
☐ ☐ ☐ ☐ ☐ ☐ ☐ ☐

Notes:

H.O.P.E. Daily Goal - High Fiber : 35g. - Oils : 2g. - Probiotics : At least 6 Billion Cultures - Enzymes : with each Meal

Date:		Day #:			Day of the week:		

FOOD			High Fiber	Omega-3 Oils	Probiotics	Enzymes

Breakfast	amount				
Snacks:					
Breakfast Totals:					

Lunch	amount				
Snacks:					
Lunch Totals:					

Dinner	amount				
Snacks:					
Dinner Totals:					

Supplements					
Description:	High Fiber	Oils	Probiotics	Enzymes

TODAY'S GRAND TOTALS

High Fiber	Probiotics
Oils	Enzymes

8 oz. glasses of water consumed

☐☐☐☐☐☐☐☐
☐☐☐☐☐☐☐☐

Notes:

H.O.P.E. Daily Goal - High Fiber : 35g. - Oils : 2g. - Probiotics : At least 6 Billion Cultures - Enzymes: with each Meal

Date:	Day #:	Day of the week:

FOOD		High Fiber	Omega-3 Oils	Probiotics	Enzymes
Breakfast	amount				
Snacks:					
Breakfast Totals:					
Lunch	amount				
Snacks:					
Lunch Totals:					
Dinner	amount				
Snacks:					
Dinner Totals:					

Supplements

Description:	High Fiber	Oils	Probiotics	Enzymes

TODAY'S GRAND TOTALS

High Fiber	Probiotics
Oils	Enzymes

8 oz. glasses of water consumed

☐☐☐☐☐☐☐☐
☐☐☐☐☐☐☐☐

Notes:

H.O.P.E. Daily Goal - High Fiber : 35g. - Oils : 2g. - Probiotics : At least 6 Billion Cultures - Enzymes: with each Meal

Date:	Day #:		Day of the week:		

FOOD		High Fiber	Omega-3 Oils	Probiotics	Enzymes
Breakfast	amount				
Snacks:					
Breakfast Totals:					
Lunch	amount				
Snacks:					
Lunch Totals:					
Dinner	amount				
Snacks:					
Dinner Totals:					

Supplements

Description:	High Fiber	Oils	Probiotics	Enzymes

TODAY'S GRAND TOTALS

High Fiber	Probiotics
Oils	Enzymes

8 oz. glasses of water consumed

☐ ☐ ☐ ☐ ☐ ☐ ☐ ☐
☐ ☐ ☐ ☐ ☐ ☐ ☐ ☐

Notes:

H.O.P.E. Daily Goal - High Fiber : 35g. - Oils : 2g. - Probiotics : At least 6 Billion Cultures - Enzymes: with each Meal

Date:	Day #:	Day of the week:

FOOD	High Fiber	Omega-3 Oils	Probiotics	Enzymes

Breakfast — amount

Snacks:				
Breakfast Totals:				

Lunch — amount

Snacks:				
Lunch Totals:				

Dinner — amount

Snacks:				
Dinner Totals:				

Supplements

Description:	High Fiber	Oils	Probiotics	Enzymes

TODAY'S GRAND TOTALS

High Fiber	Probiotics
Oils	Enzymes

8 oz. glasses of water consumed

☐ ☐ ☐ ☐ ☐ ☐ ☐ ☐
☐ ☐ ☐ ☐ ☐ ☐ ☐ ☐

Notes:

H.O.P.E. Daily Goal - High Fiber : 35g. - Oils : 2g. - Probiotics : At least 6 Billion Cultures - Enzymes : with each Meal

Date:	Day #:		Day of the week:		

FOOD		High Fiber	Omega-3 Oils	Probiotics	Enzymes
Breakfast	amount				
Snacks:					
Breakfast Totals:					
Lunch	amount				
Snacks:					
Lunch Totals:					
Dinner	amount				
Snacks:					
Dinner Totals:					

Supplements

Description:	High Fiber	Oils	Probiotics	Enzymes

TODAY'S GRAND TOTALS

High Fiber	Probiotics
Oils	Enzymes

8 oz. glasses of water consumed

☐☐☐☐☐☐☐☐
☐☐☐☐☐☐☐☐

Notes:

H.O.P.E. Daily Goal - High Fiber : 35g. - Oils : 2g. - Probiotics : At least 6 Billion Cultures - Enzymes : with each Meal

Date:	Day #:		Day of the week:

FOOD		High Fiber	Omega-3 Oils	Probiotics	Enzymes
Breakfast	amount				
Snacks:					
Breakfast Totals:					
Lunch	amount				
Snacks:					
Lunch Totals:					
Dinner	amount				
Snacks:					
Dinner Totals:					

Supplements

Description:	High Fiber	Oils	Probiotics	Enzymes

TODAY'S GRAND TOTALS

High Fiber	Probiotics
Oils	Enzymes

8 oz. glasses of water consumed

☐☐☐☐☐☐☐☐
☐☐☐☐☐☐☐☐

Notes:

Date:	Day #:	Day of the week:

FOOD	High Fiber	Omega-3 Oils	Probiotics	Enzymes

Breakfast   amount

Snacks:				
Breakfast Totals:				

Lunch   amount

Snacks:				
Lunch Totals:				

Dinner   amount

Snacks:				
Dinner Totals:				

Supplements

Description:	High Fiber	Oils	Probiotics	Enzymes

TODAY'S GRAND TOTALS

High Fiber	Probiotics
Oils	Enzymes

8 oz. glasses of water consumed

☐☐☐☐☐☐☐☐
☐☐☐☐☐☐☐☐

Notes:

H.O.P.E. Daily Goal - High Fiber : 35g. - Oils : 2g. - Probiotics : At least 6 Billion Cultures - Enzymes : with each Meal

Date:	Day #:	Day of the week:

FOOD		High Fiber	Omega-3 Oils	Probiotics	Enzymes
Breakfast	amount				
Snacks:					
Breakfast Totals:					
Lunch	amount				
Snacks:					
Lunch Totals:					
Dinner	amount				
Snacks:					
Dinner Totals:					

Supplements

Description:	High Fiber	Oils	Probiotics	Enzymes

TODAY'S GRAND TOTALS

High Fiber	Probiotics
Oils	Enzymes

8 oz. glasses of water consumed

☐☐☐☐☐☐☐☐
☐☐☐☐☐☐☐☐

Notes:

H.O.P.E. Daily Goal - High Fiber : 35g. - Oils : 2g. - Probiotics : At least 6 Billion Cultures - Enzymes: with each Meal

Date:		Day #:			Day of the week:		

FOOD			High Fiber	Omega-3 Oils	Probiotics	Enzymes

Breakfast	amount	High Fiber	Omega-3 Oils	Probiotics	Enzymes
Snacks:					
Breakfast Totals:					

Lunch	amount	High Fiber	Omega-3 Oils	Probiotics	Enzymes
Snacks:					
Lunch Totals:					

Dinner	amount	High Fiber	Omega-3 Oils	Probiotics	Enzymes
Snacks:					
Dinner Totals:					

Supplements

Description:	High Fiber	Oils	Probiotics	Enzymes

TODAY'S GRAND TOTALS

High Fiber	Probiotics
Oils	Enzymes

8 oz. glasses of water consumed

☐☐☐☐☐☐☐☐
☐☐☐☐☐☐☐☐

Notes:

H.O.P.E. Daily Goal - High Fiber : 35g. - Oils : 2g. - Probiotics : At least 6 Billion Cultures - Enzymes: with each Meal

Date:	Day #:	Day of the week:

FOOD		High Fiber	Omega-3 Oils	Probiotics	Enzymes
Breakfast	amount				
Snacks:					
Breakfast Totals:					
Lunch	amount				
Snacks:					
Lunch Totals:					
Dinner	amount				
Snacks:					
Dinner Totals:					

Supplements					
Description:	High Fiber	Oils	Probiotics	Enzymes	

TODAY'S GRAND TOTALS

High Fiber	Probiotics
Oils	Enzymes

8 oz. glasses of water consumed

Notes:

H.O.P.E. Daily Goal - High Fiber : 35g. - Oils : 2g. - Probiotics : At least 6 Billion Cultures - Enzymes: with each Mea

Date:	Day #:		Day of the week:			

FOOD		High Fiber	Omega-3 Oils	Probiotics	Enzymes
Breakfast	amount				
Snacks:					
Breakfast Totals:					
Lunch	amount				
Snacks:					
Lunch Totals:					
Dinner	amount				
Snacks:					
Dinner Totals:					

Supplements

Description:	High Fiber	Oils	Probiotics	Enzymes

TODAY'S GRAND TOTALS

High Fiber	Probiotics
Oils	Enzymes

8 oz. glasses of water consumed

☐☐☐☐☐☐☐☐
☐☐☐☐☐☐☐☐

Notes:

H.O.P.E. Daily Goal - High Fiber : 35g. - Oils : 2g. - Probiotics : At least 6 Billion Cultures - Enzymes: with each Meal

Date:	Day #:		Day of the week:

FOOD		High Fiber	Omega-3 Oils	Probiotics	Enzymes

Breakfast   amount

Snacks:					
Breakfast Totals:					

Lunch   amount

Snacks:					
Lunch Totals:					

Dinner   amount

Snacks:					
Dinner Totals:					

Supplements

Description:	High Fiber	Oils	Probiotics	Enzymes

TODAY'S GRAND TOTALS

High Fiber	Probiotics
Oils	Enzymes

8 oz. glasses of water consumed

☐☐☐☐☐☐☐
☐☐☐☐☐☐☐

Notes:

H.O.P.E. Daily Goal - High Fiber : 35g. - Oils : 2g. - Probiotics : At least 6 Billion Cultures - Enzymes: with each Me

Date:	Day #:		Day of the week:			

FOOD			High Fiber	Omega-3 Oils	Probiotics	Enzymes
Breakfast		amount				
Snacks:						
Breakfast Totals:						
Lunch		amount				
Snacks:						
Lunch Totals:						
Dinner		amount				
Snacks:						
Dinner Totals:						

Supplements					
Description:	High Fiber	Oils	Probiotics	Enzymes	

TODAY'S GRAND TOTALS

High Fiber	Probiotics
Oils	Enzymes

8 oz. glasses of water consumed

☐☐☐☐☐☐☐
☐☐☐☐☐☐☐

Notes:

H.O.P.E. Daily Goal - High Fiber : 35g. - Oils : 2g. - Probiotics : At least 6 Billion Cultures - Enzymes: with each Meal

Date:		Day #:		Day of the week:	

FOOD		High Fiber	Omega-3 Oils	Probiotics	Enzymes
Breakfast	amount				
Snacks:					
Breakfast Totals:					
Lunch	amount				
Snacks:					
Lunch Totals:					
Dinner	amount				
Snacks:					
Dinner Totals:					

Supplements					
Description:	High Fiber	Oils	Probiotics	Enzymes	

TODAY'S GRAND TOTALS

High Fiber	Probiotics
Oils	Enzymes

8 oz. glasses of water consumed

☐☐☐☐☐☐☐☐
☐☐☐☐☐☐☐☐

Notes:

H.O.P.E. Daily Goal - High Fiber : 35g. - Oils : 2g. - Probiotics : At least 6 Billion Cultures - Enzymes: with each Meal

Date:	Day #:	Day of the week:

FOOD		High Fiber	Omega-3 Oils	Probiotics	Enzymes
Breakfast	amount				
Snacks:					
Breakfast Totals:					
Lunch	amount				
Snacks:					
Lunch Totals:					
Dinner	amount				
Snacks:					
Dinner Totals:					

Supplements

Description:	High Fiber	Oils	Probiotics	Enzymes

TODAY'S GRAND TOTALS

High Fiber	Probiotics
Oils	Enzymes

8 oz. glasses of water consumed

☐☐☐☐☐☐☐☐
☐☐☐☐☐☐☐☐

Notes:

H.O.P.E. Daily Goal - High Fiber : 35g. - Oils : 2g. - Probiotics : At least 6 Billion Cultures - Enzymes: with each Meal

Date:	Day #:	Day of the week:

FOOD		High Fiber	Omega-3 Oils	Probiotics	Enzymes

Breakfast — amount

Snacks:

Breakfast Totals:

Lunch — amount

Snacks:

Lunch Totals:

Dinner — amount

Snacks:

Dinner Totals:

Supplements						TODAY'S GRAND TOTALS

Description:	High Fiber	Oils	Probiotics	Enzymes

TODAY'S GRAND TOTALS

High Fiber	Probiotics

Oils	Enzymes

8 oz. glasses of water consumed

☐☐☐☐☐☐☐☐☐
☐☐☐☐☐☐☐☐

Notes:

PART III

H.O.P.E. FORMULA RESOURCES

H.O.P.E. Meals vs. Non H.O.P.E. Meals

	H.O.P.E. meals	non-H.O.P.E. meals
Breakfast:	1/2 cup Steel Cut Oatmeal 1 cup mixed fruit 1 cup yogurt	Bacon and eggs White toast
Lunch:	spinach salad with grilled chicken	Hamburger French Fries
Dinner:	Salmon w/ lemon Brown rice Mixed green salad	Fried Chicken Mashed Potatoes Corn

Recap: How to use the "Food List"

Favorite Food	Measure	Fiber	Omega-3 Oils	Probiotics	Enzymes
F & G		grams	grams	value 0-3	*
Figs, dried	2 figs	1.6	0	0	*

How to use the "Favorite Food List" section. This section lists alphabetically some popular foods that are found in standard diets. Each item is identified with Fiber, Omega 3 Oils, Probiotic and Enzyme content. Both Fiber and Omega 3 Oil content are listed in grams. However, the probiotic content is given a value from 0-3 (as used in section 3 above) with 3 being the highest. This number identifies low to high probiotic content. The asterisk indicates that the food contains enzymes.

* All values are approximate according to the USDA National Nutrient Database unless otherwise noted.

Favorite Food	Measure	Fiber	Omega-3 Oils	Probiotics	Enzymes
A		grams	grams	value 0-3	*
Alfalfa Seeds, sprouted, raw	1 cup	1	0	0	*
Almonds, raw	1 oz. (aprox 23)	3.3	0	0	*
Apple, raw, with skin	1 medium	3.3	0.01	0	*
Applesauce, unsweetened	1 cup	2.9	0	0	
Apricot, raw	1 apricot	0.7	0	0	*
Artichoke, cooked	1 medium	6.5	0.02	0	
Avocado (source avocado.org)	1 medium	15	aprox. 16	0	*

Favorite Food	Measure	Fiber	Omega-3 Oils	Probiotics	Enzymes
B		grams	grams	value 0-3	*
Bagel, plain, enriched	4" bagel	2	0.1	0	
Banana	1 medium	3.1	0.03	0	*
Barley, pearled, cooked	1 cup	6	0.03	0	
Beans, black, cooked	1 cup	15	0.18	0	
Beans, kidney, cooked	1 cup	11	0.24	0	
Beans, navy, cooked	1 cup	13.4	0.22	0	
Beans, pinto, cooked	1 cup	11	0.4	0	
Beef, cooked	4 oz	0	0.2	0	
Beets, raw	1 cup	3.8	0	0	*
Blackberries, raw	1 cup	7.6	0.13	0	*
Blueberries, raw	1 cup	3.5	0.08	0	*
Bread, wheat	1 slice	2	0	0	
Broccoli, raw	1 cup	2.4	0	0	*
Brussels sprouts, cooked	1 cup	4.1	0.26	0	

C

Favorite Food	Measure	Fiber	Omega-3 Oils	Probiotics	Enzymes
C		grams	grams	value 0-3	*
Cabbage, cooked	1 cup	2.9	0.16	0	
Cabbage, raw	1 cup	2	0.03	0	*
Cantalope, raw	1 cup	1.4	0.07	0	*
Carrots, cooked	1 cup	4.7	0	0	
Carrots, raw	1 cup	3.6	0	0	*
Cauliflower, raw	1 cup	2.5	0.07	0	*
Celery, raw	1 stalk	0.6	0	0	*
Chicken, cooked	4 oz	0	0.07	0	
Cheese, cheddar	1 oz	0	0.1	0	*
Cherries, raw, w/pits	1 cup	2.5	0.03	0	*
Chickpeas (garbanzos), cooked	1 cup	12.5	0.07	0	
Corn, cooked	1 ear	2.9	0.01	0	
Couscous, cooked	1 cup	2.2	0	0	

Favorite Food	Measure	Fiber	Omega-3 Oils	Probiotics	Enzymes
D & E					
Dates, dried	1 cup	14.2	0	0	*
Egg, regular, cooked	1 egg	0	0.07	0	
Egg, omega -3, cooked	1 egg	0	0.15	0	

Favorite Food	Measure	Fiber	Omega-3 Oils	Probiotics	Enzymes
F & G		grams	grams	value 0-3	*
Figs, dried	2 figs	1.6	0	0	*
Fish, anchovies (source EUFIC)	1 cup	0	1.7	0	
Fish, cod	1 cup	0	0.14	0	
Fish, halibut	1 cup	0	0.57	0	
Fish, mackerel	1 cup	0	1.21	0	
Fish, salmon, wild	1 cup	0	2.19	0	
Fish, sardines (source EUFIC)	1 sardine	0	1.4	0	
Flaxseeds, raw, whole	4 oz	1.9	1.55	0	*
Grapefruit, raw, all areas	1/2 grapefruit	<1	0	0	*
Grapes, red or green	1 cup	<1	0.02	0	*

Favorite Food	Measure	Fiber	Omega-3 Oils	Probiotics	Enzymes
H, I, & J					
Hummus	1 tbsp	<1	n/a	0	*
Honeydew, raw	1 cup	1.4	0.06	0	*
K					
Kale, cooked	1 cup	2.6	0.13	0	
Kefir (source from Lifeway.net)	1 cup	3	N/A	3	*
Kiwi fruit, raw	1 medium	2.3	0.03	0	*

Favorite Food	Measure	Fiber	Omega-3 Oils	Probiotics	Enzymes
L		grams	grams	value 0-3	*
Lentils, cooked	1 cup	15.6	0.07	0	
Lettuce, iceberg	2 cup	1.3	0.05	0	*
Lettuce, romaine	2 cup	2	0.11	0	*
Lima beans, cooked	1 cup	13.2	0.09	0	
M & N					
Macaroni, cooked, elbow	1 cup	2.5	0.03	0	
Macaroni, cooked, wheat	1 cup	3.9	0.01	0	
Mangos, raw	1 fruit	3.7	0.07	0	*
Miso	1 cup	14.8	1.24	3	*
Mushrooms, portobella	1 cup	1.3	0	0	*
Mustard greens, cooked	1 cup	2.8	0.03	0	
Nectarine, raw	1 fruit	2.3	0	0	*

Favorite Food	Measure	Fiber	Omega-3 Oils	Probiotics	Enzymes
O					
Oat bran, raw	1 cup	14.5	0.11	0	*
Oatmeal, steel cut	1/2 cup	8 to 11	0	0	
Oil, olive	1 tbsp	0	0.11	0	
Oil, vegetable	1 tbsp	0	0.31	0	
Oil, canola	1 tbsp	0	1.29	0	
Okra, cooked	1 cup	4	0.07	0	
Onions, raw	1 cup	2.2	0	0	*
Orange, raw	1 fruit	3.4	0.01	0	*
P					
Papaya, raw	1 cup	2.5	0.03	0	*
Peach, raw	1 fruit	1.5	0	0	*
Pear, raw	1 fruit	5.1	0	0	*
Peas, green, cooked	1 cup	8.8	0.03	0	
Pineapple, raw	1 cup	2.2	0.03	0	*
Plantains, raw	1 medium	4.1	0.04	0	*
Potato, baked, with skin	1 medium	3.6	0.01	0	*
Popcorn, air-popped	1 cup	1.2	0	0	

Favorite Food	Measure	Fiber	Omega-3 Oils	Probiotics	Enzymes
R					
Raisins, seedless	1 cup	5.4	0.01	0	*
Raspberries, raw	1 cup	8	0.16	0	*
Refried beans	1 cup	13.4	0.05	0	
Rice, brown	1 cup	3.5	0.03	0	
Rice, white	1 cup	0.6	0.02	0	
S					
Sauerkraut	1 cup	3.5	0.04	2	*
Spinach, cooked	1 cup	4.3	0.15	0	
Spinach, raw	1 package (10 oz)	6.2	0.39	0	*
Squash, summer, raw	1 cup	1.2	0.06	0	*
Strawberries, raw	1 cup	3	0.1	0	*
Sweet potato, cooked	1 medium	3.8	0	0	*

Favorite Food	Measure	Fiber	Omega-3 Oils	Probiotics	Enzymes
T					
Tomatoes, red, raw	1 medium	1.5	0	0	*
Tofu, raw, firm	1 slice (2 oz)	0.1	0.45	2	*
U,V & W					
Walnuts, raw, shelled	1 cup	6.7	9.08	0	*
Wheat germ	1 cup	15.2	0.83	0	*
X,Y & Z					
Yogurt, plain	1 cup	0	0.06	3	*
Zucchini, raw	1 cup	1.2	0.05	0	*

Recap: How to graph

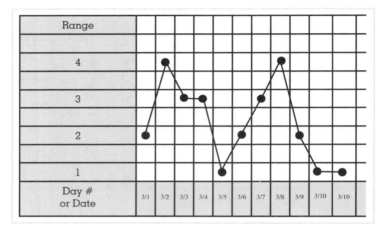

This section will allow you to track your daily progress visually. The left side of the graph is numbered from 1-4. This number represents how many parts of the formula (H.O.P.E.) that you achieved for that day. The bottom of the graph gives you a box to put in the date. Using the goals for each day and your daily grand totals, fill in the graph appropriately.

Range									
4									
3									
2									
1									
Day # or Date									

Range									
4									
3									
2									
1									
Day # or Date									

Range		4		3		2		1		Day # or Date

Range		4		3		2		1		Day # or Date

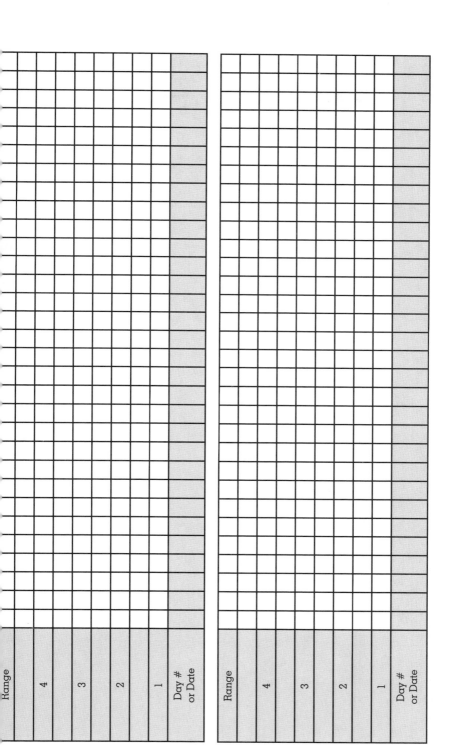

2006

JANUARY
M	T	W	T	F	S	S
						1
2	3	4	5	6	7	8
9	10	11	12	13	14	15
16	17	18	19	20	21	22
23	24	25	26	27	28	29
30	31					

FEBRUARY
M	T	W	T	F	S	S
		1	2	3	4	5
6	7	8	9	10	11	12
13	14	15	16	17	18	19
20	21	22	23	24	25	26
27	28					

MARCH
M	T	W	T	F	S	S
		1	2	3	4	5
6	7	8	9	10	11	12
13	14	15	16	17	18	19
20	21	22	23	24	25	26
27	28	29	30	31		

APRIL
M	T	W	T	F	S	S
					1	2
3	4	5	6	7	8	9
10	11	12	13	14	15	16
17	18	19	20	21	22	23
24	25	26	27	28	29	30

MAY
M	T	W	T	F	S	S
1	2	3	4	5	6	7
8	9	10	11	12	13	14
15	16	17	18	19	20	21
22	23	24	25	26	27	28
29	30	31				

JUNE
M	T	W	T	F	S	S
			1	2	3	4
5	6	7	8	9	10	11
12	13	14	15	16	17	18
19	20	21	22	23	24	25
26	27	28	29	30		

JULY
M	T	W	T	F	S	S
					1	2
3	4	5	6	7	8	9
10	11	12	13	14	15	16
17	18	19	20	21	22	23
24	25	26	27	28	29	30
31						

AUGUST
M	T	W	T	F	S	S
	1	2	3	4	5	6
7	8	9	10	11	12	13
14	15	16	17	18	19	20
21	22	23	24	25	26	27
28	29	30	31			

SEPTEMBER
M	T	W	T	F	S	S
				1	2	3
4	5	6	7	8	9	10
11	12	13	14	15	16	17
18	19	20	21	22	23	24
25	26	27	28	29	30	

OCTOBER
M	T	W	T	F	S	S
						1
2	3	4	5	6	7	8
9	10	11	12	13	14	15
16	17	18	19	20	21	22
23	24	25	26	27	28	29
30	31					

NOVEMBER
M	T	W	T	F	S	S
		1	2	3	4	5
6	7	8	9	10	11	12
13	14	15	16	17	18	19
20	21	22	23	24	25	26
27	28	29	30			

DECEMBER
M	T	W	T	F	S	S
				1	2	3
4	5	6	7	8	9	10
11	12	13	14	15	16	17
18	19	20	21	22	23	24
25	26	27	28	29	30	31

2007

JANUARY
M	T	W	T	F	S	S
1	2	3	4	5	6	7
8	9	10	11	12	13	14
15	16	17	18	19	20	21
22	23	24	25	26	27	28
29	30	31				

FEBRUARY
M	T	W	T	F	S	S
			1	2	3	4
5	6	7	8	9	10	11
12	13	14	15	16	17	18
19	20	21	22	23	24	25
26	27	28				

MARCH
M	T	W	T	F	S	S
			1	2	3	4
5	6	7	8	9	10	11
12	13	14	15	16	17	18
19	20	21	22	23	24	25
26	27	28	29	30	31	

APRIL
M	T	W	T	F	S	S
						1
2	3	4	5	6	7	8
9	10	11	12	13	14	15
16	17	18	19	20	21	22
23	24	25	26	27	28	29
30						

MAY
M	T	W	T	F	S	S
	1	2	3	4	5	6
7	8	9	10	11	12	13
14	15	16	17	18	19	20
21	22	23	24	25	26	27
28	29	30	31			

JUNE
M	T	W	T	F	S	S
				1	2	3
4	5	6	7	8	9	10
11	12	13	14	15	16	17
18	19	20	21	22	23	24
25	26	27	28	29	30	

JULY
M	T	W	T	F	S	S
						1
2	3	4	5	6	7	8
9	10	11	12	13	14	15
16	17	18	19	20	21	22
23	24	25	26	27	28	29
30	31					

AUGUST
M	T	W	T	F	S	S
		1	2	3	4	5
6	7	8	9	10	11	12
13	14	15	16	17	18	19
20	21	22	23	24	25	26
27	28	29	30	31		

SEPTEMBER
M	T	W	T	F	S	S
					1	2
3	4	5	6	7	8	9
10	11	12	13	14	15	16
17	18	19	20	21	22	23
24	25	26	27	28	29	

OCTOBER
M	T	W	T	F	S	S
1	2	3	4	5	6	7
8	9	10	11	12	13	14
15	16	17	18	19	20	21
22	23	24	25	26	27	28
29	30	31				

NOVEMBER
M	T	W	T	F	S	S
			1	2	3	4
5	6	7	8	9	10	11
12	13	14	15	16	17	18
19	20	21	22	23	24	25
26	27	28	29	30		

DECEMBER
M	T	W	T	F	S	S
					1	2
3	4	5	6	7	8	9
10	11	12	13	14	15	16
17	18	19	20	21	22	23
24	25	26	27	28	29	30
31						

JANUARY

M	T	W	T	F	S	S
	1	2	3	4	5	6
	8	9	10	11	12	13
	15	16	17	18	19	20
	22	23	24	25	26	27
	29	30	31			

FEBRUARY

M	T	W	T	F	S	S
				1	2	3
4	5	6	7	8	9	10
11	12	13	14	15	16	17
18	19	20	21	22	23	24
25	26	27	28	29		

MARCH

M	T	W	T	F	S	S
					1	2
3	4	5	6	7	8	9
10	11	12	13	14	15	16
17	18	19	20	21	22	23
24	25	26	27	28	29	30
31						

APRIL

M	T	W	T	F	S	S
	1	2	3	4	5	6
	8	9	10	11	12	13
	15	16	17	18	19	20
	22	23	24	25	26	27
	29	30				

MAY

M	T	W	T	F	S	S
			1	2	3	4
5	6	7	8	9	10	11
12	13	14	15	16	17	18
19	20	21	22	23	24	25
26	27	28	29	30	31	

JUNE

M	T	W	T	F	S	S
						1
2	3	4	5	6	7	8
9	10	11	12	13	14	15
16	17	18	19	20	21	22
23	24	25	26	27	28	29
30						

JULY

M	T	W	T	F	S	S
	1	2	3	4	5	6
	8	9	10	11	12	13
	15	16	17	18	19	20
	22	23	24	25	26	27
	29	30	31			

AUGUST

M	T	W	T	F	S	S
				1	2	3
4	5	6	7	8	9	10
11	12	13	14	15	16	17
18	19	20	21	22	23	24
25	26	27	28	29	30	31

SEPTEMBER

M	T	W	T	F	S	S
1	2	3	4	5	6	7
8	9	10	11	12	13	14
15	16	17	18	19	20	21
22	23	24	25	26	27	28
29	30					

OCTOBER

M	T	W	T	F	S	S
		1	2	3	4	5
	7	8	9	10	11	12
	14	15	16	17	18	19
	21	22	23	24	25	26
	28	29	30	31		

NOVEMBER

M	T	W	T	F	S	S
					1	2
3	4	5	6	7	8	9
10	11	12	13	14	15	16
17	18	19	20	21	22	23
24	25	26	27	28	29	30

DECEMBER

M	T	W	T	F	S	S
1	2	3	4	5	6	7
8	9	10	11	12	13	14
15	16	17	18	19	20	21
22	23	24	25	26	27	28
29	30	31				

JANUARY

M	T	W	T	F	S	S
			1	2	3	4
	6	7	8	9	10	11
	13	14	15	16	17	18
	20	21	22	23	24	25
	27	28	29	30	31	

FEBRUARY

M	T	W	T	F	S	S
						1
2	3	4	5	6	7	8
9	10	11	12	13	14	15
16	17	18	19	20	21	22
23	24	25	26	27	28	

MARCH

M	T	W	T	F	S	S
						1
2	3	4	5	6	7	8
9	10	11	12	13	14	15
16	17	18	19	20	21	22
23	24	25	26	27	28	29
30	31					

APRIL

M	T	W	T	F	S	S
		1	2	3	4	5
	7	8	9	10	11	12
	14	15	16	17	18	19
	21	22	23	24	25	26
	28	29	30			

MAY

M	T	W	T	F	S	S
				1	2	3
4	5	6	7	8	9	10
11	12	13	14	15	16	17
18	19	20	21	22	23	24
25	26	27	28	29	30	31

JUNE

M	T	W	T	F	S	S
1	2	3	4	5	6	7
8	9	10	11	12	13	14
15	16	17	18	19	20	21
22	23	24	25	26	27	28
29	30					

JULY

M	T	W	T	F	S	S
		1	2	3	4	5
	7	8	9	10	11	12
	14	15	16	17	18	19
	21	22	23	24	25	26
	28	29	30	31		

AUGUST

M	T	W	T	F	S	S
					1	2
3	4	5	6	7	8	9
10	11	12	13	14	15	16
17	18	19	20	21	22	23
24	25	26	27	28	29	30
31						

SEPTEMBER

M	T	W	T	F	S	S
	1	2	3	4	5	6
7	8	9	10	11	12	13
14	15	16	17	18	19	20
21	22	23	24	25	26	27
28	29	30				

OCTOBER

M	T	W	T	F	S	S
			1	2	3	4
	6	7	8	9	10	11
	13	14	15	16	17	18
	20	21	22	23	24	25
	27	28	29	30	31	

NOVEMBER

M	T	W	T	F	S	S
						1
2	3	4	5	6	7	8
9	10	11	12	13	14	15
16	17	18	19	20	21	22
23	24	25	26	27	28	29
30						

DECEMBER

M	T	W	T	F	S	S
	1	2	3	4	5	6
7	8	9	10	11	12	13
14	15	16	17	18	19	20
21	22	23	24	25	26	27
28	29	30	31			

To order additional journals...

Please call :

Renew Your Life Press at 1-(800)-830-4778
or visit your local health food store.

Renew Your Life Press
2076 Sunnydale Blvd.
Clearwater, Fl 33765
www.hopeformula.com